Lesson Masters A

THE UNIVERSITY OF CHICAGO SCHOOL MATHEMATICS PROJECT

ALGEBRA

SCOTTFORESMAN INTEGRATED MATHEMATICS

Further practice on
SPUR objectives

ScottForesman

A Division of HarperCollinsPublishers

ScottForesman
Editorial Offices: Glenview, Illinois
Regional Offices: Sunnyvale, California • Tucker, Georgia
Glenview, Illinois • Oakland, New Jersey • Dallas, Texas

Contents

Pages	Contents
1-141	Lesson Masters
142-177	Answers for Lesson Masters

ISBN: 0-673-45770-2

Copyright © 1996

Scott, Foresman and Company, Glenview, Illinois
All Rights Reserved.
Printed in the United States of America.

2 3 4 5 6 - BI - 0 0 9 9 9 8 9 7 9 6

LESSON MASTER

1-1
A

Questions on SPUR Objectives
See pages 65-68 for objectives.

Vocabulary

1. What is an *equation*? _____

2. What does the symbol "≤" mean? _____

3. Write an inequality that compares $\frac{4}{7}$ and $\frac{1}{2}$ and that

   a. uses the symbol "<." _____

   b. uses the symbol ">." _____

4. Which of the symbols $=, \neq, \approx, >, \geq, <,$ and $\leq$
   make a true statement when written in the blank?

   $$\frac{2}{3} \underline{\quad ? \quad} .66$$ _____

5. Let p = the population of the United States.

   a. Write an inequality for this statement:

      The population of the United
      States is greater than 250 million. _____

   b. Give a number that is a solution
      to the sentence in Part a. _____

6. Give an example of an open sentence.

   _____

7. Let B = Bill's batting average. Write a sentence in words that
   fits the algebraic sentence $B > .275$.

   _____

Skills Objective A

8. Which of the numbers 2, 4, and 6
   are solutions to $n + 5 = 2 \cdot n - 1$?

   _____

9. Which of the numbers 2, 3, and 4
   are solutions to $4 \cdot k + 8 > 16$?

   _____

10. Give three solutions to the open sentence $m < 6.5$.

    _____   _____   _____

11. Find both solutions to $x^2 = 81$.   _____   _____

12. Give an example of an inequality
    for which 10 is a solution. _____

1

LESSON MASTER 1-2 A

Properties Objective E

1. Give an example of a number that is an integer. _____

2. Give an example of a number that is not an integer. _____

3. Give an example of a number that is
   an integer but is not a whole number. _____

4. Is the interval that is the graph of $5 \leq n \leq 18.5$
   open, *closed*, or *neither* open nor closed? _____

Uses Objective I

Multiple choice. **In 5–6, choose the most reasonable domain**
for the variable.

   (a) set of integers   (b) set of real numbers

   (c) set of positive integers   (d) set of positive real numbers

5. y = the year a battle was fought by the Roman army _____

6. s = the number of hot dogs sold at a baseball park _____

Representations Objective L

In 7–8, graph the solution set on a number line.

7. $n < 2$, when n is an integer

8. $1.2 \leq y < 1.8$ when y is a
   real number

Multiple choice. **In 9–12, tell which domain was used in the**
graph of $y < 2$.

   (a) set of integers   (b) set of real numbers

   (c) set of positive integers   (d) set of positive real numbers

9. 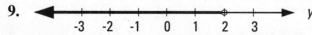 _____

10. 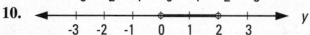 _____

11. 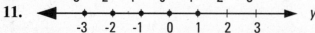 _____

12. 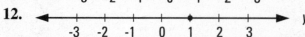 _____

Name _____

LESSON MASTER **1-3 A**

Questions on SPUR Objectives
See pages 65-68 for objectives.

Skills Objective B

1.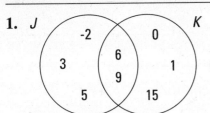

For the Venn diagram at the left, list the elements of

a. $J \cup K$. _____

b. $J \cap K$. _____

2. Let $R = \{5, 10, 15, 20\}$ and $T = \{11, 12, 13, 14, 15\}$.

a. Give the union of R and T. _____

b. Give the intersection of R and T. _____

3. Let $A =$ the set of divisors of 12 and $B =$ the set of divisors of 30. List the elements of $A \cap B$. _____

Properties Objective E

4. Give an example of two sets of E and F for which $E \cap F = \emptyset$.

$E =$ _____ $F =$ _____

5. Let $P \cap Q = \{1, 2\}$, $P \cup Q = \{1, 2, 3, 4\}$. Draw a Venn diagram to show sets of P and Q that fit this description. There are several possible diagrams.

Representations Objective L

6. Graph the solution sets. For a domain, use the set of real numbers.

a. $n > 10$

b. $n \le 24$

c. $n > 10$ and $n \le 24$

d. $n < 10$ or $n \ge 24$

7. In 1993, an unmarried U.S. taxpayer paid 28% income tax on earnings described by the inequality $\$22,101 < x \le \$53,500$.

a. Graph this interval.

b. Describe the interval with two inequalities linked by the word "and."

LESSON MASTER

1-4
A

Questions on SPUR Objectives
See pages 65-68 for objectives.

Vocabulary

1. Give an example of a numerical expression. _____

2. Give an example of an algebraic expression. _____

3. What does it mean to "evaluate an expression"?

   _____

Skills Objective C

4. Evaluate $12y + 3$ when

   a. $y = 4$. _____ **b.** $y = 2.5$. _____ **c.** $y = 0$. _____

For 5–10, if the expression is algebraic write "algebraic." If the expression is numerical, evaluate it.

5. $\dfrac{3 + 15}{2(3)}$ _____

6. $4(2 + 7) - k$ _____

7. $40 - 3(11)$ _____

8. $2(3 + 2)^2 + 9$ _____

9. $a - \dfrac{4}{n}$ _____

10. $3^5 - 5^3$ _____

11.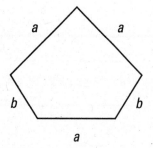

   The perimeter of this pentagon is $3a + 2b$. Find the perimeter when $a = 15.4$ and $b = 6.5$.

   _____

12. What is the value of the BASIC expression $(2 * 8 + 5)/(30 - 23)$? _____

13. Write a key sequence to enter the following expression into a calculator. $\dfrac{40 \cdot 2 + 8}{4^2}$

   _____

14. **a.** Evaluate $10y^3$ when $y = 2$.   **b.** Evaluate $(10y)^3$ when $y = 2$.

   _____   _____

   c. Find a value for y so that the value of $10y^3$ is the same as the value for $(10y)^3$. _____

LESSON MASTER **1-5 A**

Vocabulary

1. **a.** *Multiple choice.* Which of the equations
   below is a formula for y in terms of
   other variables? _____

   (a) $Ax + By = C$ (b) $x = \dfrac{C - By}{A}$ (c) $y = \dfrac{C - Ax}{B}$

   b. What are the other variables? _____

Uses Objective J

2. A concession stand sells sandwiches and cold drinks. The
   price P of an order, including sales tax, is given by the formula

   $$P = 1.05(3S + 75D)$$

   where S = the number of sandwiches ordered and D = the
   number of drinks ordered. Find the cost of each order, rounded
   up to the next cent.

   a. 4 sandwiches and 5 drinks _____

   b. 6 drinks _____

3. Use the formula $V = \frac{4}{3}\pi r^3$ for
   the volume of a sphere. Find the volume
   of a softball with radius 3.8 in. _____

4. Suppose you have n dollars and you save 8 dollars each week
   for w weeks. The amount of money m you have will be given by

   $$m = n + 8w.$$

   How much money will you have after

   a. 5 weeks if you start with $25? _____

   b. one year if you start with $60? _____

5. The cost C for y cubic yards of cement is given by
   $$C = 37.50y + 65.$$
   Find the cost of 6.5 cubic yards of cement. _____

LESSON MASTER 1-6 A

Vocabulary

1. What is the name for the symbol "$\sqrt{}$"? _____

2. Give an example of two numbers that
   a. are perfect squares. _____

   b. are *not* perfect squares. _____

Skills Objectives C and D

In 3 and 4, give a. the exact square roots of the given number and b. the approximate square roots, rounded to the nearest hundredth.

3. 41 a. _____   4. 325 a. _____

       b. _____   b. _____

5. The area of a square is 517 sq ft. Give
   a. the exact length of a side of the square. _____

   b. the length of a side rounded
      to the nearest hundredth. _____

In 6–12, evaluate without a calculator.

6. $\sqrt{49} + \sqrt{1}$ _____   7. $\sqrt{36} + \sqrt{64}$ _____   8. $\sqrt{36 + 64}$ _____

9. $8\sqrt{25}$ _____   10. $11\sqrt{5} \cdot \sqrt{5}$ _____   11. $(\sqrt{12})^2$ _____

12. Evaluate each expression to the nearest thousandth
    when $s = 10$ and $t = 50$.

    a. $\sqrt{st}$ _____   b. $s\sqrt{t}$ _____

13. If an object is dropped and it falls d feet in t seconds, then $t = \sqrt{\dfrac{d}{16}}$.

    If an object were dropped from the top of
    the Empire State building, which is 1250 ft tall,
    how long would it take to hit the ground? _____

Properties Objective F

14. What does the Square of the Square Root Property tell you
    about $\sqrt{y^2} \cdot \sqrt{y^2}$?

    _____

LESSON MASTER

1-7
A

Vocabulary

In 1 and 2, consider the pattern $a\sqrt{4} = \sqrt{a \cdot 4}$. When $a = 1$, this is true, because $1 \cdot \sqrt{4} = \sqrt{1 \cdot 4}$. When $a = 9$, this is false, because $9\sqrt{4} \neq \sqrt{9 \cdot 4}$. Which value of a

1. gives an *instance* of $a\sqrt{4} = \sqrt{a \cdot 4}$?   _____

2. gives a *counterexample* to $a\sqrt{4} = \sqrt{a \cdot 4}$?   _____

Properties Objective G

In 3–5, give two instances of the pattern.

3. $\dfrac{x^3}{x} = x^2$

_____   _____

4. $5(a + b) = 5a + 5b$

_____

_____

5. h hours and m minutes is $60h + m$ minutes.

_____

_____

In 6 and 7, give a counterexample to show that the pattern is not always true.

6. $n^2 = 2n$ _____

7. $2a + b = 2b + a$ _____

► **LESSON MASTER 1-7 A** *page 2*

Properties Objective H

8.

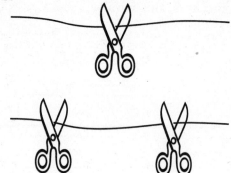

A piece of string is cut into pieces.
Describe the following pattern using
one variable.

1 cut makes 1 + 1 pieces of string.

2 cuts make 2 + 1 pieces of string.

3 cuts make 3 + 1 pieces of string.

---

9. a. Describe this pattern with one variable.

$\frac{1}{6} < 6$

$\frac{1}{8.5} < 8.5$

$\frac{1}{57} < 57$ _____

   b. Find another integer that gives
   an instance of this pattern. _____

   c. Find an integer that gives
   a counterexample to the pattern. _____

   d. Find a non-integer that gives
   a counterexample to the pattern. _____

10. Use two variables to describe this pattern.

$3 + 3 + 8 = 2 \cdot 3 + 8$

$55 + 55 + 1 = 2 \cdot 55 + 1$

$.4 + .4 + .6 = 2 \cdot .4 + .6$ _____

LESSON MASTER 1-8 A

Vocabulary

In 1–3, name **a.** the hypotenuse and **b.** the legs.

1.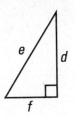

2.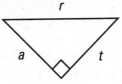

3.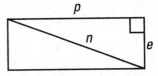

a. _____   a. _____   a. _____

b. _____   b. _____   b. _____

Uses Objective K

4. To drive from town A to town B you can travel 8 miles east and then 4 miles south.

   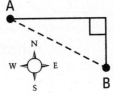

   a. How long is the drive from A to B?   _____

   b. A shortcut path from A directly to B is shown by the dotted line. How long is the shortcut?   _____

   c. How much shorter is the shortcut than the road that goes east and then south?   _____

5.

   A road construction worker needs to make a diagonal brace to hold a sign. The pole is 3 ft high, and the bottom of the brace will be 3 ft from the pole. To the nearest inch, how long must the brace be?

   _____

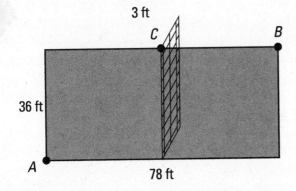

In 6 and 7, use the diagram of a doubles tennis court, which measures 78 ft by 36 ft.

6. To the nearest foot, how far is it from *A* to *B*?

   _____

7. To the nearest foot, how far is it from *A* to *C*?

   _____

LESSON MASTER

Properties Objective G

1. 5 squares   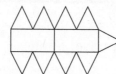 6 squares   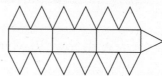 7 squares

   a. Sketch the next two instances in the pattern above.

   b. Fill in the chart below.

Number of Squares	5	6	7	8	9	. . .	n
Perimeter						. . .	

2. Triangles and blocks are used to make the pattern below.

   a. Draw the fourth instance.

   b. How many blocks will be needed to make the hundredth instance? How many will be triangles? Explain how you got your answers.

   _____

   _____

   _____

Properties Objective H

For 3 and 4, use the chart at the right.

3. Does the equation $b = 7a$ describe the numbers in the table? Explain why or why not.

a	1	2	3	4
b	7	8	9	10

   _____

   _____

4. Does the equation $b = a + 6$ describe the numbers in the table? Explain why or why not.

   _____

   _____

Name _____

5. The diagram below shows a brick wall made from whole
and half-bricks.

1 row
5 bricks and 1 half-brick

2 rows
10 bricks and 2 half-bricks

3 rows
15 bricks and 3 half-bricks

   a. Let r = the number of rows, b = the number of whole bricks,
and h = the number of half-bricks. Find two formulas: one
which describes the relationship between r and b, and one
which describes the relationship between r and h.

_____ _____

   b. If the wall has 12 rows, how many whole and half-bricks
will be used?

_____

In 6-8, use the pattern below.

1 square
2 triangles
perimeter = 6

2 squares
4 triangles
perimeter = 10

3 squares
6 triangles
perimeter = 14

4 squares
8 triangles
perimeter = 18

6. Let s = the number of squares and t = the number of triangles.
Describe the relationship between s and t.

_____

7. Explain why the formula $p = 6s$ does not relate the perimeter p
of the figure to the number of squares.

_____

_____

8. A correct formula giving the perimeter in terms of the number
of squares is $p = 4s + 2$. Show that the formula works for a figure
with 6 squares by drawing the figure and finding its perimeter.

_____

LESSON MASTER

2-1
A

Questions on SPUR Objectives
See pages 136-138 for objectives.

Skills Objective F

In 1–3, tell whether the statement illustrates the Commutative Property of Multiplication or the Associative Property of Multiplication.

1. $3(7x) = 21x$

2. $1.5(2y^3) = 1.5(y^3 \cdot 2)$

_____   _____

3. Twenty 10-ounce bars of chocolate contain the same amount of chocolate as ten 20-ounce bars. _____

In 4–7, simplify.

4. $50x^2 \cdot 2 \cdot 19$ _____

5. $8a \cdot 7b$ _____

6. $10x \cdot 2xy \cdot 3xz$ _____

7. $\frac{2}{5}p \cdot 5q$ _____

Uses Objective G

In 8 and 9, find the area of the shaded region.

8.

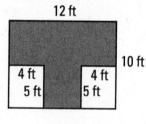

9.

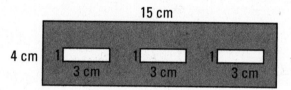

_____   _____

10. A building code requires that the windows in a room have glass area equal to 15% of the floor area. An architect's plan has two 3-ft-by-4-ft windows in a 12-ft-by-15-ft room. Does this plan meet the code? Why or why not?

_____

_____

11. How many boxes $1'' \times 2'' \times 3''$ can be packed in a carton 2 ft $\times$ 3 ft $\times$ 5 ft? _____

Representations Objective J

12.

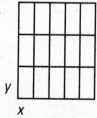

Each small rectangle has length y and width x. The large rectangle is made up of 15 of the small rectangles.

a. Express the area of the large rectangle as length times width. _____

b. Simplify your answer to Part a. _____

LESSON MASTER

2-2
A

Questions on SPUR Objectives
See pages 136-138 for objectives.

Properties Objective F

In 1–6, give the reciprocal.

1. $\frac{2}{3}$ _____   2. $1\frac{2}{5}$ _____   3. $\frac{-4}{p}$ _____

4. $\frac{1}{10}$ _____   5. -0.25 _____   6. $\frac{6}{a+b}$ _____

7. Write a key sequence you could use to find the reciprocal of 1.333 on a calculator that has no reciprocal key.

_____

8. *Multiple choice.* Which equation means that x and y are reciprocals?   _____

(a) $\frac{x}{y} = 1$ (b) $1x = y$ (c) $x + y = 1$

(d) $xy = 1$ (e) $\frac{x}{y} = \frac{y}{x}$

In 9–12, a. tell whether the two numbers are reciprocals, and b. briefly explain why or why not.

9. 5 and 0.2   a. _____   b. _____

10. $-\frac{1}{3}$ and 3   a. _____   b. _____

11. -1 and -1   a. _____   b. _____

12. 100,000 and 0.000001   a. _____   b. _____

In 13–16, a. simplify, and b. name the property you used.

13. $10(3x - 3x)$

a. _____   b. _____

14. $(a + b) \cdot \frac{1}{a+b}$

a. _____   b. _____

15. $\frac{4.7x^2}{4.7x^2} \cdot 5$

a. _____   b. _____

16. $(3t + 1)(2t - 2)(t + 3)(0)$

a. _____   b. _____

LESSON MASTER

2-3 A

Skills Objective A

In 1–4, use the Equal Fractions Property to simplify.

1. $\dfrac{5t}{3tb}$ 2. $\dfrac{24a^2}{8}$ 3. $\dfrac{5000x}{2000xy}$ 4. $\dfrac{85m^3n}{100m^2x}$

_____   _____   _____   _____

In 5–16, multiply. Simplify the product where possible.

5. $\dfrac{2}{3} \cdot \dfrac{x}{8}$ 6. $\dfrac{2x}{3} \cdot \dfrac{15}{x}$ 7. $\dfrac{15a}{2a} \cdot \dfrac{1}{5}$

_____   _____   _____

8. $\dfrac{x^2}{8y} \cdot \dfrac{9}{4x^2}$ 9. $6 \cdot \dfrac{2x}{3}$ 10. $\dfrac{1}{0.85} \cdot 0.85t$

_____   _____   _____

11. $\dfrac{nx}{5} \cdot \dfrac{11}{ny}$ 12. $45 \cdot \dfrac{7}{15s}$ 13. $\dfrac{1200a}{11x} \cdot \dfrac{55x^2}{400a^2}$

_____   _____   _____

14. $\dfrac{7200r}{35r^2} \cdot \dfrac{5}{1200}$ 15. $\dfrac{5}{2n} \cdot \dfrac{3x}{25} \cdot \dfrac{4n}{9x}$ 16. $\dfrac{10y}{3} \cdot \dfrac{30x}{7y} \cdot \dfrac{42}{500}$

_____   _____   _____

17. The largest rectangle at the right has base x and height y.

   a. If all the smallest rectangles have
   the same dimensions, what is the
   area of the shaded region?   _____

   b. What product of algebraic fractions
   is represented by the product of length
   and width of the shaded region?   _____

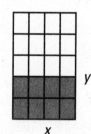

18. An architect designed a seminar room to be two fifths as long
   and one third as wide as an adjoining lecture hall. Compare
   the areas of the two rooms.

   _____

   _____

   _____

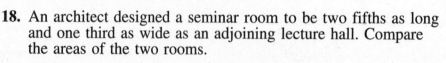

LESSON MASTER

2-4 A

Uses Objective H

1. One of the longest trips reported for a single fill-up was about 1690 miles in a Toyota LandCruiser which had a total fuel capacity of 38.2 gallons in two tanks. Compute the mpg (miles per gallon) for this trip.

   _____

2. A construction company asserts that it can build one mile of road every 10 days. How many miles can it build in one day?

   _____

3. A ream of paper is 500 sheets. Four reams weight 20 pounds. What is the weight of 5000 sheets of paper?

   _____

4. A 250-gram serving of spaghetti with meatballs contains 330 calories in food energy.

   a. What is the number of calories per gram?

   _____

   b. A 150-pound person will burn about 9.5 calories for every minute of jogging. How long will it take to burn off the calories from a 250-gram serving of spaghetti?

   _____

5. The Japanese *Shinkansen* (bullet train) averages about 165 kilometers per hour between Tokyo and Osaka. What is this rate in meters per second?

   _____

6. The label on a frozen turkey says "Roast thawed turkey at 325° for 20 minutes per pound." How many *hours* will it take to roast a 22-pound turkey?

   _____

LESSON MASTER

2-5 A

Skills Objective B

1. Write as a product involving a negative rate. The Army Corps of Engineers expects the Mississippi River to drop 2.5 cm per day after spring floods. What is the expected drop in 14 days? _____

2. Show that $-\frac{4}{5}$ is the reciprocal of $-\frac{5}{4}$. _____

In 3–11, multiply. Simplify where possible.

3. $-5 \cdot -7$

4. $-3x \cdot 2$

5. $3x \cdot -2b$

6. $-6 \cdot \frac{2}{3} \cdot -5$

7. $2a \cdot -5a \cdot 17a$

8. $-\frac{2}{3} \cdot -\frac{3}{5}$

9. $\frac{2x}{7x} \cdot \frac{-3x}{8x}$

10. $\frac{-3}{x} \cdot \frac{x}{-3}$

11. $(-5a)^2$

12. Evaluate $2x + 3$ when $x = -5$.

13. Evaluate $\frac{3y}{5} \cdot y$ when $y = -1$.

14. Evaluate $-5t^2 + 3t$ when $t = 2$.

Properties Objective F

In 15–20, tell whether the value of the expression is positive or negative.

15. $(-1)^5$

16. $(-3)^4$

17. $(-3)(-2)(-5)(-\frac{1}{3})$

18. -7^2

19. $(-8)^9$

20. $(11)(-4)(7)(0.01)(-6)$

21. *Multiple choice.* Which of the following equals the opposite of x? _____

(a) $1 - x$ (b) $\frac{1}{x}$ (c) $1x$ (d) $-1x$

LESSON MASTER 2-6 A

Questions on SPUR Objectives
See pages 136-138 for objectives.

Skills Objective C

In 1–7, solve and check the equation.

1. $\frac{1}{5}y = -12$

2. $8x = 128$

3. $-9a = 162$

4. $\frac{3}{4}x = 15$

5. $-7s = 6.3$

6. $-\frac{5}{9} = \frac{2d}{3}$

7. $20\left(\frac{1}{2}m\right) = 510$

Properties Objective F

8. If you ask for a "baker's dozen" donuts, you get 13 donuts. This can be expressed as an equation: 1 baker's dozen = 13 donuts. Tell how you could apply the Multiplication Property of Equality to this equation to find out how many donuts are in 5 baker's dozens.

_____

_____

9. Tell which property justifies each step in the solution of $80r = 200$.

Multiplicative Identity Property of 1   **Multiplication Property of Equality**

Associative Property of Multiplication   **Property of Reciprocals**

$$80r = 200$$

$$\frac{1}{80} \cdot 80r = \frac{1}{80} \cdot 200 \qquad \text{_____}$$

$$\left(\frac{1}{80} \cdot 80\right)r = \frac{200}{80} \qquad \text{_____}$$

$$1r = 25 \qquad \text{_____}$$

$$r = 25 \qquad \text{_____}$$

Uses Objective H

10. The equation $p = rt$ gives the total pay for an employee who has worked t hours at r dollars per hour.

a. Use this formula to write an equation that can be used to find the hourly pay rate for an employee who earned $107 for 20 hours of work. _____

b. Solve the equation from Part a for r.   **c.** Solve $p = rt$ for r.

_____   _____

LESSON MASTER

2-7 A

Skills Objective C

In 1–6, solve and check where possible.

1. $27x = 0$

_____   _____
solution   check

2. $0a = 15$

_____   _____
solution   check

3. $-x = 11.5$

_____   _____
solution   check

4. $0y = 0$

_____   _____
solution   check

5. $0 = (15 - 15)t$ _____

solution   check
            _____

6. $-(-x) = -19$

_____   _____
solution   check

In 7–12, solve the equation.

7. $-\frac{1}{3}a = 20$ **8.** $-\frac{1}{3}b = 0$ **9.** $0c = 20$

10. $5.3d = -0.371$ **11.** $-(5.3e) = -0.371$ **12.** $5.3f = 0$

Properties Objective F

13. Explain why one of the equations in 7–9 doesn't have a solution.

_____

_____

_____

LESSON MASTER

2-8 A

Skills Objective D

In 1–8, solve and check the inequality.

1. $15m \geq 45$

2. $60 < 12x$

3. $-11y > 33$

4. $54 \geq -9z$

5. $-\frac{2}{3}n > 30$

6. $-\frac{9}{10} \leq -\frac{3}{100}x$

7. $.18a \geq .09$

8. $3.9b < -19.5$

Properties Objective F

9. If $-x > a$, then x __?__ $-a$ $(<, >, =)$ _____

10. What inequality results if both sides of $-\frac{5}{8}x \leq -15$ are multiplied by $-\frac{8}{5}$?   _____

11. Explain why the opposite of a number less than 200 must be greater than -200.

_____

_____

_____

▶ **LESSON MASTER 2-8 A** *page 2*

Uses Objective G

12. A roll of wallpaper is 1.5 ft wide and 24 ft long.
At least how many rolls are needed to cover a wall
that is 15 ft long and 8 ft high?

    a. Write an inequality for the number   _____
       of rolls of paper.

    b. Solve the inequality.   _____

    c. Answer the question.   _____

Uses Objective H

13. A class has accumulated $110.50 in its party fund.
How many large pizzas can the class purchase
at $10.95 per pizza?

    a. Write an inequality for the number   _____
       of pizzas that can be purchased.

    b. Solve the inequality.   _____

    c. Answer the question.   _____

14. Mr. Johnson wants to travel at least 300 miles on
the first day of his cross-country trip. How many
hours must he travel if he can average 45 miles
per hour?

    a. Write an inequality for the number   _____
       of hours he must travel.

    b. Solve the inequality.   _____

    c. Answer the question.   _____

LESSON MASTER **2-9 A**

Uses Objective I

1. A family who lives in a house in a historical district must paint their house with colors appropriate to the area in the early nineteenth century. The village permits houses of white, cream, or grey; windows of white or black; and shutters of green or black. Use a tree diagram or a list to show all ways the house could be painted.

2. A pizzeria offers pizzas with three crust options: thin, thick, or stuffed; and four sizes: individual, small, medium, and large. How many types of pizza are possible?

   _____

3. The big breakfast at Dot's Restaurant offers diners one choice from each of the following:

   - eggs (fried, poached, scrambled, over-easy)
   - potatoes or grits
   - toast (wheat, white, or muffin)
   - meat (sausage, ham, or bacon)
   - juice (orange, grapefruit, tomato, apricot, grape, apple)

   How many different big breakfasts are there?

   _____

4. A small business has its own internal phone system. Each phone number is four digits long. The first digit must be 2 to indicate an internal call, and the second digit cannot be 0. How many internal phone numbers are possible for this company?

   _____

5. Some license plates contain three letters followed by three numbers, such as MOM104 or WIN085.

   a. How many different plates are possible?

                                                  _____

   b. How many are there if you can't have letters repeat as the M does in MOM104?

                                                  _____

6. Write a problem using the Multiplication Counting Principle that has as its answer $3 \cdot 5 \cdot 2$.

_____

_____

_____

7. A quiz has three multiple-choice questions, each with four options A, B, C, and D. The quiz also has five true-false questions.

   a. How many different ways are there for a student to answer the questions on the quiz?

                                                  _____

   b. How many different ways would there be for a student to answer a quiz if there were x multiple-choice questions followed by y true-false questions?

                                                  _____

8. **a.** How many batting lineups can a 10-member softball team have?

                                                  _____

   b. How many lineups are there if the pitcher must bat last and the best batter (who is not the pitcher) must bat fourth?

                                                  _____

Name _____

LESSON MASTER **2-10 A**

Questions on SPUR Objectives
See pages 136-138 for objectives.

Vocabulary

1. Use a factorial symbol to write an expression
   for $8 \cdot 7 \cdot 6 \cdot 5 \cdot 4 \cdot 3 \cdot 2 \cdot 1$.   _____

Skills Objective E

2. Evaluate $n!$ when $n = 12$.   3. Which is larger, $5! \cdot 6!$ or $(5 \cdot 6)!$?

   _____   _____

4. Explain how to simplify $\frac{50!}{48!}$ without a calculator.

   _____

In 5 and 6, find n.

5. $n! = 120$ _____   6. $n! = 40,320$ _____

Uses Objective I

**In 7 and 8, use this information: A toy company is designing a
new game that has 5 buttons of different colors. One player
presses all 5 buttons in a particular order, and then his opponent
must repeat the order.**

7. How many orders are possible with five buttons?

   _____

8. An advanced version of the game has 7 buttons instead of 5.
   How many *more* orders are possible in the advanced version?

   _____

9. Eight sprinters are running in a race. If there are
   no ties, in how many ways can

   a. first place be awarded?   _____

   b. first and second places be awarded?   _____

   c. first, second, and third places be awarded? _____

   d. all eight places be awarded?   _____

LESSON MASTER

3-1 A

Skills Objective A

In 1–4, simplify the expression.

1. $(-8 + -6) + 4$

2. $-8 + (n + -21)$

3. $(x + 9) + (y + -20)$

_____   _____   _____

4. In a magic square each row, column, and diagonal has the same sum. Fill in the blanks in the square at the right so the sum is -6.

	-10	4
-8		

Properties Objective E

In 5 and 6, tell which property of addition is illustrated.

5. $(2x + 5) + (3y + 2) = (3y + 2) + (2x + 5)$

_____

6. $8 + (2n + 9) = (8 + 2n) + 9$

_____

7. Give three instances of the Associative Property of Addition.

_____

_____

Uses Objective G

In 8–10, write an addition expression or equation to describe each situation.

8. This year the company's profits were P dollars. Profits are expected to drop D dollars next year, and then increase by $5000 the following year.   _____

9. The president's popularity rating was 58% last month, but it rose $r\%$ and is now $n\%$.   _____

10. Television shows are rated each week. At the beginning of the month, World-Wide news had a rating of 8.2. During the next four weeks the rating went up a points, then down b points, up 5 points, and up c points. At the end of this time, the rating reached the program's all-time high of 11.3.

_____

LESSON MASTER

3-2
A

Skills Objective A

In 1–4, simplify the expression.

1. $(4x + -12) + 12$ _____

2. $-3.2 + -(-3.2)$ _____

3. $-(-8x)$ _____

4. $-15 + (3y + 15)$ _____

Skills Objective B

In 5–10, solve and check the equation.

5. $y + 18 = -4$ 6. $-4a = 628$ 7. $48 = n + -10$

8. $y + \frac{3}{11} = -\frac{8}{11}$ 9. $\frac{7}{8} = \frac{3}{4}m$ 10. $624.5 + x = 453.9$

Properties Objective E

In 11–13, give a. another instance of the property
illustrated and b. the name of the property.

11. $-(-76) = 76$ a. _____   b. _____

12. $0 + \frac{2}{3} = \frac{2}{3}$ a. _____   b. _____

13. $\pi + (-\pi) = 0$ a. _____   b. _____

In 14 and 15, give the number that should be added to both
sides to solve the equation quickly.

14. $82 = y + 24$ _____   15. $-12 + x = 92$ _____

Uses Objective G

For 16 and 17, write an addition equation to describe the
situation and solve the equation to answer the question.

16. During the summer of 1993 the Mississippi River flooded its
banks. In St. Louis, the water was 17 feet above flood stage when
it crested at 47 feet. What is considered flood stage at St. Louis?

_____   _____
            equation   answer

17. The low temperature of the day occurred at 4 A.M.. By 10 A.M.
it had risen 12° to -9°. What was the 4 A.M. temperature?

_____   _____
            equation   answer

LESSON MASTER 3-3 A

Questions on SPUR Objectives
See pages 210-213 for objectives.

Representations Objective I

1. a. Draw a graph for the data below, showing cars per
100 people on the horizontal axis and miles
traveled per 1,000 people on the vertical axis.

COUNTRY	CARS PER 100 PEOPLE	MILES PER PERSON
United States	58	8,260
New Zealand	51	4,120
Germany	49	4,342
Canada	47	5,302
Australia	46	5,766
France	41	4,584
Austria	38	4,413
United Kingdom	38	3,881
Netherlands	36	3,731
Denmark	32	4,351
Spain	29	1,573
Japan	27	2,621
Ireland	22	4,062

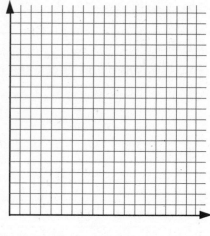

b. Describe any trend you see in the data. Are there
any countries that do not follow this trend?

_____

_____

c. If a country has 55 cars per 100 persons,
estimate the distance traveled per person. _____

**In 2–4, use this graph for 13-year-old students
from six countries. For each country, a point shows
the percent of students who watch 5 or more
hours of TV and who do not do their homework.**

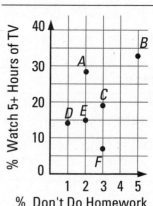

2. For Canadian students, 3% don't do
their homework and 19% watch
5 or more hours of TV. Which
point represents Canada?   _____

3. In the country represented by
point *F*, about what percent of
students don't do their homework?   _____

4. Describe any trends you see in the graph.

_____

_____

LESSON MASTER **3-4 A**

Representations Objective J

1. a. On the coordinate grid at the right, graph $B'A'R'K'S'$, the image of sliding pentagon *BARKS* 2 units right and 5 units up.

   b. Slide $B'A'R'K'S'$ 6 units left and 2 units up. Label the image $B''A''R''K''S''$.

   c. Use your answer to Part **b** to find the coordinates of point B''.

   _____

   d. Point $B = (-1, -1)$. Explain how to find the coordinates of point B'' without drawing $B'A'R'K'S'$ and $B''A''R''K''S''$.

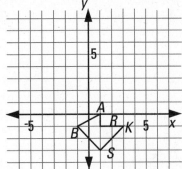

   _____

   _____

2. The point $(7, -4)$ is translated 2 units left and 1 unit down. What are the coordinates of the image? _____

In 3 and 4, give the image of point $Q = (x, y)$ under a slide

3. 3 units right and 5 units down.   4. 9 units left.

   _____   _____

In 5–7, give a formula for a slide for which the image of the point $(-4, -1)$ will be

5. in Quadrant II.   6. in Quadrant IV.   7. on the y-axis.

   _____   _____   _____

In 8–10, use the graph at the right. It shows P and P', its image under a slide.

8. Describe the slide: __?__ units to the (left or right) and __?__ units (up or down).

   _____ _____

9. Point J is shown on the graph. Plot J', its image under the same slide under which the image of P is P'.

10. Fill in the blanks to describe the slide algebraically: The image of (x, y) is

    $(x + $ _____ $, y + $ _____ $)$.

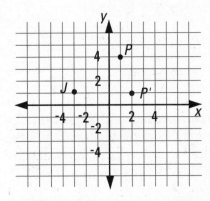

LESSON MASTER 3-5 A

Skills Objective B

In 1–6, solve and check the equation.

1. $-12x + 2 = 50$

2. $-20 = 2n$

3. $-4 + \frac{5}{6}a = -31$

4. $144 = 18k + -54$

5. $-28a = 63$

6. $.03y + 1.2 = -6.3$

Uses Objective G

7. For a school sale, Janine made several batches of cookies, with about 60 cookies per batch. Other students contributed 350 cookies. Altogether there were 650 cookies for the sale. How many batches did Janine make? _____

8. Pedro ordered x boxes of paper at $25.89 per box and a printer ribbon which cost $7.29. The total for the order was $214.41. How many boxes of paper were ordered? Write an equation to describe this situation. Then solve the equation to find the answer.

_____   _____
equation   answer

Representations Objective K

9.

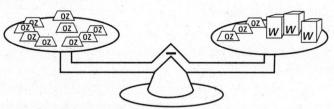

a. What equation is pictured by the diagram at the left?

_____

b. What is the weight of one box?

_____

10. a. Sketch a balance-scale diagram for $4w + 1 = 13$.

b. What is the solution to the equation? _____

LESSON MASTER

3-6
A

Vocabulary

1. Give an example of *like terms*.

_____

2. Give an example of *unlike terms*.

_____

Skills Objective A

In 3–8, simplify the expression.

3. $12n + 18n$

_____

4. $8x(5x) + 12x^2$

_____

5. $5a + 2b + 3b + -8a$

_____

6. $y + y + 3$

_____

7. $(4n^2 + 9) + (-3n^2 + 4)$

_____

8. $4(11x) + 21x$

_____

Skills Objective B

9. Solve and check $10n + -8n = 622$.   _____

Properties Objective E

In 10–11, tell what property has been applied.

10. $a + a = 1a + 1a$

_____

11. $\frac{3}{5}x + \frac{1}{5}x = \frac{4}{5}x$

_____

Uses Objective G

12. Each week Maria earns $8 more than Dave at the store where they work. Their total pay for the week will be $60. Write and solve an equation for this situation to find each person's pay.

_____   _____
      equation   answer

Representations Objective K

13. a. What is the area of the left rectangle?   _____

b. What is the area of the right rectangle?   _____

c. Give the total area of the largest rectangle in simplified form.   _____

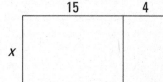

LESSON MASTER **3-7 A**

Skills Objective A

In 1–6, simplify the expression.

1. $4(x + y + 8)$

2. $n(n - 12)$

3. $10a(3a - 8)$

4. $-2(x + 15) + 4$

5. $9x + 15x - 4$

6. $-6(n + 1) + (11n + 1)$

Skills Objective B

In 7–10, solve the equation and check your result.

7. $2.4 = 6(n - 1.3)$

8. $8(2x + 5) - 16 = 72$

9. $\frac{3}{4}(3x + 8) = 15$

10. $4(1.5y + -7) + 2y = -4$

Properties Objective E

In 11–13, tell whether the Distributive Property has been applied in the equation. Write *yes* or *no*.

11. $3y + 8y + 4 = 11y + 4$

12. $9(8 + 2x) + 3 = 3 + 9(8 + 2x)$

13. $4(2a + b + 5c) = 8a + 4b + 20c$

Properties Objective F

14. Sam's regular rate of pay is $6.20 per hour. If he is paid time and a half for overtime, what is his overtime rate of pay? Explain how you can mentally compute your answer.

_____

_____

_____

15. The freshman class has 99 students. Mentally compute the cost if the entire class buys

   a. T-shirts at $8 each.   _____

   b. yearbooks at $20 each.   _____

Representations Objective K

In 16 and 17, express the area of each largest rectangle as a. length times width and b. the sum of areas of smaller rectangles.

16.

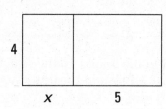

17.

   a. _____   **a.** _____

   b. _____   **b.** _____

LESSON MASTER 3-8 A

Questions on SPUR Objectives
See pages 210-213 for objectives.

Uses Objective H

In 1–9, use the sequence of designs shown below.

1. Draw the next design in the sequence.   1st   2nd   3rd

2. Complete the chart at the right to show the perimeters of the first through fifth designs.

3. If the perimeter of a figure is 84, what would the perimeter of the next design be?   _____

Design Number	Perimeter
1	16
2	
3	
4	
5	

4. If n = the design number and p = the perimeter, then the relationship between them is described by $p = 12 + 4n$.

   a. Find the perimeter of the 15th design.   _____

   b. Which design has a perimeter of 140?   _____

5. Complete the chart at the right.

6. If one design has 49 squares, how many squares will the next design have?

   _____

n(Design Number)	s(Number of Squares)
1	
2	
3	
4	
5	

7. Fill in the blanks in the equation to make a formula for this pattern.

   $s =$ _____ $+$ _____ n

8. How many squares would then be in the 12th design?   _____

9. Which design is made up of 59 squares?   _____

In 10–12, use the salad price list at the right.

10. How much would a 6-oz salad cost?   _____

11. How does the price change as the weight increases?

   _____

   _____

Salad Weight	Price
1 oz	$ .65
2 oz	$ .90
3 oz	$1.15
4 oz	$1.40
5 oz	$1.65

12. Write an equation for the cost of a salad that weighs w oz.   _____

LESSON MASTER 3-9 A

Skills Objective C

In 1–4, find the sum.

1. $-\frac{6}{7} + \frac{11}{7}$ _____

2. $6\frac{3}{4} + \frac{3}{4}$ _____

3. $\frac{5}{3n} + \frac{-25}{3n} + \frac{-4}{3n}$ _____

4. $\frac{3n + 8}{4} + \frac{n + 3}{4}$ _____

5. What common denominator would you use to add $\frac{a}{10}$ and $\frac{5a}{4}$? _____

In 6–9, use a common denominator to write as a single fraction.

6. $\frac{x}{10} + \frac{8x}{5}$

7. $n + \frac{n}{4}$

8. $-\frac{2y}{15} + \frac{5y}{6}$

9. $5a + \frac{2a}{7}$

_____   _____   _____   _____

10. Simplify $\frac{-3}{8}x + \frac{1}{4}x$. _____

In 11–13, use this sequence: $\frac{1}{10}, \frac{1}{5}, \frac{3}{10}, \frac{2}{5}, \frac{1}{2}, \frac{3}{5}, \frac{7}{10}, \frac{4}{5}, \frac{9}{10}, 1$

11. What is the difference between each term
and the term which precedes it? _____

12. Write the next ten terms in the sequence.

_____

13. Describe any patterns you see in the sequence.

_____

_____

_____

Properties Objective E

**In 14–16, simplify the sum. Tell whether you used the
Distributive Property for Adding Fractions. Write *yes* or *no*.**

14. $\frac{a}{c} + \frac{b}{c}$ _____ _____

15. $\frac{4}{5} + \left(x + -\frac{4}{5}\right)$ _____ _____

16. $\frac{5x}{3} + \frac{2x}{3}$ _____ _____

LESSON MASTER **3-10 A**

Vocabulary

1. How is the Addition Property of Inequality different from the Multiplication Property of Inequality?

_____

_____

_____

Skills Objective D

2. Chuck solved $-5x + 8 < -47$. His solution was $x < 11$. Chuck did not check his answer, so he did not realize that his answer was wrong.

   a. Write a check to show that his answer is wrong. _____

   b. Write a note to explain to Chuck what he did wrong.

   _____

   _____

In 3–6, solve each inequality and check your result.

3. $-2y + 8 \geq 26$

4. $-2 + 8n \geq 26$

5. $-6 < -n + 9$

6. $4\left(\frac{1}{2}x + 17\right) \leq 164$

Uses Objective G

7. For the last thirty days Al's Auto's sold an average of C cars each day and broke the previous record of 484 cars sold in 30 days.

   a. Write an inequality to describe this situation. _____

   b. On the average, how many cars were sold each day during the last 30 days? _____

▶ **LESSON MASTER 3-10 A** *page 2*

8. When the temperature is $T°$ Fahrenheit, a certain
   type of tree cricket chirps about C times per
   minute, and $T = \frac{1}{4}C + 37$. Yesterday's temperature
   stayed below 90°F. How fast were crickets chirping?

   _____

Representations Objective K

9.

   a. Write an inequality to describe this diagram. _____

   b. Solve the inequality from Part **a.** _____

Representations Objective L

10. *Multiple choice.* Which of the graphs below shows
    the solutions of $-3x + 8 < 38$? _____

   (a) ←———⊕———→ x
              10

   (b) ←———⊕———→ x
              -10

   (c) ←———●———→ x
              -10

   (d) ←———●———→ x
              10

In 11–13, graph all solutions.

11. $2.4n + -1.8 > -4.2$

12. $16 > -2x + 30$

   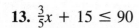

13. $\frac{3}{5}x + 15 \le 90$

   ←————————————————————→

LESSON MASTER

Skills Objective A

In 1–6, simplify the expression.

1. $3 - -25$

2. $-8 - 10$

3. $4x + 3x - 8x$

_____   _____   _____

4. $15y - -y$

5. $\frac{5}{8}t - \frac{1}{2}t - \frac{3}{8}t$

6. $-\frac{6n}{x} - \frac{5n}{x}$

_____   _____   _____

7. Evaluate $x^2 - y$ when $x = -6$ and $y = -1$.   _____

8. Evaluate $5 - 10 + 15 - 20 + 25 - 30 + \ldots + 95 - 100$.   _____

9. Let S = the amount of money Scrooge has and M = the amount of money Midas has. If $S - M < 0$, which man has more money? Explain how you know.

_____

_____

Properties Objective E

In 10–13, use this table showing a person's weight from week to week. The numbers in the Change row show how the weight compares to the weight the previous week. Complete the table.

Week	1	2	3	4	5	6
Weight	178	175	176	172	174	177
Change		-3	1	**10.** ?	**11.** ?	**12.** ?

10. _____   11. _____   12. _____

13. How could you find the change for Week 2

    a. using subtraction?   _____

    b. using addition?   _____

In 14–16, rewrite each subtraction as an addition.

14. $-3 - 5 + n$

15. $6 + 11 - -30$

16. $5x - 12 - -7y$

_____   _____   _____

LESSON MASTER 4-2 A

Questions on SPUR Objectives
See pages 278-281 for objectives.

Uses Objective H

In 1–3, use the table at the right. Remember that a negative profit is a loss.

Profits for World-Wide Widget (in millions)	
DOMESTIC	**FOREIGN**
Factory A: 13.2	Factory E: -6.4
Factory B: 8.6	Factory F: -1.3
Factory C: -1.9	Factory G: -15.0
Factory D: .4	

1. How much more did the most profitable factory earn than the least profitable?

   _____

2. What was the range of earnings for the domestic factories?

   _____

3. What was the range of earnings for the foreign factories?

   _____

4. Let K = Kendra's age and M = Marsha's age. Kendra is younger than Marsha. Which is positive, $M - K$ or $K - M$?   _____

In 5 and 6, let R = Ryan's age now. Write an expression for Ryan's age

5. 8 years ago.   _____

6. 3 years from now.   _____

In 7 and 8, write a subtraction expression for the length of the segment marked with a question mark (?).

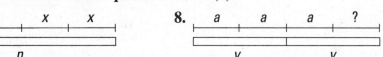

7.
8.

   _____

9. Home-Bake Bread launched a new advertising campaign and is keeping track of the number of loaves sold.

Week 1	2,452
Week 2	3,621
Week 3	4,102
Week 4	3,015

   a. What was the change from Week 2 to Week 3?   _____

   b. What was the change from Week 3 to Week 4?   _____

In 10 and 11 let A = Alissa's age. Steve's age is $A - 11$ and Beth's age is $A + 4$.

10. Arrange the three ages in order from youngest to oldest.   _____

11. The oldest person is y years older than the youngest. Find the value of y and explain your reasoning.

    _____

    _____

LESSON MASTER 4-3 A

Skills Objective B

In 1–6, solve and check the equation.

1. $8x - 13 = 51$

2. $1.5 = -1.2n - 0.9$

3. $6 - y = -20$

4. $\frac{3}{7}b - 9 = 2$

5. $3(22v - 1) = 162$

6. $-6(m + 2) + 4 = 36$

Skills Objective C

7. *Skill sequence.* Solve.

 a. $5x - 40 = 125$ _____

 b. $5x - 40 < 125$ _____

 c. $5 - 40x = 125$ _____

 d. $5 - 40x < 125$ _____

In 8–10, a. solve and b. graph.

8. $-8 \leq 4d - 26$ a. _____   b. ⟵—————————⟶

9. $15 + 2(5z - 50) < 68$ a. _____   b. ⟵—————————⟶

10. $9n - 54 > -36$ a. _____   b. ⟵—————————⟶

Uses Objectives H and I

In 11–13, write an equation or an inequality to describe the situation. Then answer the question.

11. Suppose the temperature started at 10° and dropped 4° each hour. After x hours it was -14°. How many hours had elapsed?

 _____   _____
        sentence   answer

12. When a certain number is multiplied by 12 and then the product is subtracted from 21, the answer is -63. What is the number?

 _____   _____
        sentence   answer

13. Of the 478 people who started the race, quite a few dropped out and fewer than 350 crossed the finish line. How many people dropped out?

 _____   _____
        sentence   answer

LESSON MASTER 4-4 A

Representations Objective K

In 1–4, use the spreadsheet at the right. It shows weather data for an afternoon.

	A	B	C
1	TIME	TEMP	RAIN
2	1	87	0
3	2	88	0
4	3	88	.5
5	4	84	1.2
6	5	79	.1
7	6	77	0
8			

1. What is in cell C3?

   _____

2. Which cell contains the number 79?

   _____

3. Suppose that the formula =C2+C3+C4+C5+C6+C7 is entered in cell C8.

   a. What value will appear in cell C8? _____

   b. What real-life quantity does this formula calculate? _____

4. What formula can be entered in cell B8 to find the average temperature for the afternoon? _____

In 5–8, use this information: Subscribers to the *Midvale Times* can have the paper delivered each day for $4.00 per week or on Sundays only for $1.25 per week. The spreadsheet below shows the number and type of subscriptions for the four areas of town.

	A	B	C	D
1	ROUTE	DAILY	SUNDAY ONLY	WEEKLY $
2	north	128	34	554.50
3	east	161	45	700.25
4	south	103	21	438.25
5	west	115	28	
6	total	507	128	

5. What formula can be used in cell C6 to calculate the total number of subscribers who get the Sunday paper only? _____

6. a. What formula can be entered in cell D5
to find the total cost for the papers
delivered in the western route? _____

b. What number will appear in cell D5? _____

7. Give two different formulas that could be entered in
cell D6 to give the total cost for all four routes.

_____   _____

8. If the east route increases to 165 daily subscriptions
so that 165 is in cell B3, which other cells would change?

_____

In 9 and 10, use the spreadsheet below. Barb uses it to keep track
of her money. She has columns for her weekly allowance, her pay
for mowing lawns, and baby-sitting, and her weekly expenses.

	A	B	C	D	E	F
1	START	ALLOWANCE	MOW LAWNS	BABYSIT	SPENDING	END
2	48.15	5.00	15.00	3.25	4.88	66.52
3	66.52	5.00	10.00	0.00	12.92	68.60
4	68.60	5.00	10.00	6.50	43.21	46.89

9. Write a formula for cell F2 which finds
Barb's balance at the end of the week. _____

10. Barb decides to add a column to show how the
amount she has changes from week to week.

a. If cell G3 contains the formula $=F3-F2$,
what number will appear in cell G3? _____

b. If cell G4 contains the formula $=F4-F3$,
what number will appear in cell G4? _____

c. Why do the answers to Parts a and b have different signs?

_____

_____

11. In a spreadsheet, suppose cell B9 contains the
number 28 and cell C9 contains the number 6. If
cell G9 contains the formula $=(B9-2*C9)\^2$,
what number will appear in cell G9? _____

LESSON MASTER

4-5 A

Skills Objective D

1. *Multiple choice.* Which expression is *not* equal to -(8x − 10)? _____
   (a) -8x − 10   (b) -8x − -10
   (c) -8x + 10   (d) -2(4x − 5)

2. Juan simplified -6(2x − 4) and got -12x − 24. Write a note to Juan to convince him that his answer is wrong by substituting 3 for x in both expressions.

   _____

   _____

   _____

In 3–10, simplify the expression.

3. -2(-2x + 25)   4. -3(n − 2x + 11)   5. -24k − (4k + 3)

   _____   _____   _____

6. (5a + 9) − (4a − 2)   7. (2y − 16) − (y + 8)   8. 6n − 4(n + 11)

   _____   _____   _____

9. $\dfrac{3a}{4} - \dfrac{5a - 8}{12}$ 10. $\dfrac{x + 4}{5} - \dfrac{x + 5}{6} - \dfrac{5 - x}{3}$

   _____   _____

In 11–14, solve and check the equation.

11. 9x − (3 + 5x) = 17   12. 50 = -5(3x + 8) − (7x − 24)

13. 20 − 2(x + 41) = -38   14. -4(x + 8) + 3x = 47

LESSON MASTER

4-6
A

Questions on SPUR Objectives
See pages 278-281 for objectives.

Representations Objective L

1. Yvonne is 2 years younger than her sister Xandra. Let Yvonne's age be y and Xandra's age be x.

   a. Which equation describes this situation, $y = x + 2$ or $y = x - 2$? _____

   b. Fill in the chart with some possible ages for the girls.

Xandra x	Yvonne y	Ordered Pairs (x, y)
5		
6		
7		
8		
9		
10		

   c. Graph possible pairs of ages for the girls.

   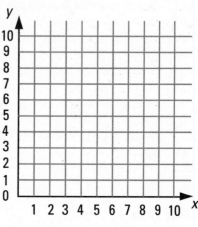

   d. How old were the girls when the sum of their ages was 16? _____

2. Consider the equation $x + y = 7$.

   a. Write four pairs (x, y) that satisfy $x + y = 7$.

x	y	(x, y)

   b. Graph *all* ordered pairs satisfying the equation on the grid at the right.

   b.

   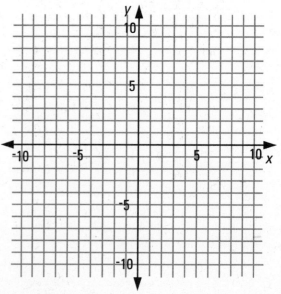

LESSON MASTER 4-7 A

Properties Objective F

1. Use a protractor and the angle at the right.

   a. Find its measure. _____

   b. Draw a complement.

   c. Draw a supplement.

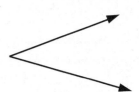

In 2–4, the measure of an angle is given. Find the measure of a. a complement and b. a supplement.

2. 18° a. _____   3. 124° a. _____   4. g° a. _____

   b. _____   b. _____   b. _____

5. a. Write an equation to describe the situation shown in the diagram.

   _____

   b. Find the value of x. _____ c. m $\angle ABC =$ _____

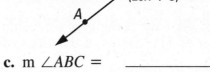

6. Let $x =$ the measure of $\angle A$. The measure of $\angle B$ is 6 more than three times the measure of $\angle A$. $\angle A$ and $\angle B$ are complements. Write and solve an equation to find the measure of each angle.

   _____   _____
            equation   answer

7. Write an expression to represent the measure of $\angle GEM$ in terms of a and b.

   _____

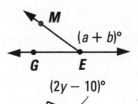

8. Use the triangle at the right.

   a. Write an equation relating the angles.

   _____

   b. Find the value of y. _____

   c. Find the measures of the angles. _____

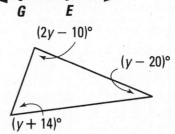

9. In the triangle at the right, label each unlabeled angle with its measure.

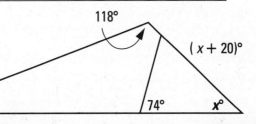

LESSON MASTER 4-8 A

Properties Objective G

In 1–3, write an expression for the length of $\overline{BC}$ in terms of x and y.

1.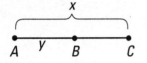

2.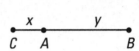

3.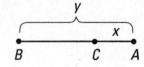

_____   _____   _____

4. Fill in the blanks. Use the triangle at the right.

   a. $x <$ _____   **b.** $x >$ _____

   c. _____ $< x <$ _____

5. Suppose you know that in $\triangle PET$, $PE = 29.6$ and $ET = 21.8$. The length of PT is between what two numbers?   _____

6. Give an example of three numbers that *cannot* be the lengths of the sides of a triangle.   _____

7.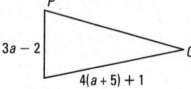

Refer to the triangle at the left. Fill in the blanks with simplified expressions.

_____ $< PQ <$ _____

Uses Objective J

8. Millford is 83 miles from Rockton and Milford is 130 miles from Portland. Is it possible that Rockton is 210 miles from Portland? Explain why or why not.

_____

_____

_____

9. It takes Rhonda 15 minutes to walk to Amber's house and 24 minutes to walk to Tanya's house. Assuming Amber and Rhonda walk at the same speed, how long would it take Amber to walk to Tanya's house?   _____

LESSON MASTER

4-9
A

Representations Objective L

In 1–3, use these charges for Pat's pizza: $6 for a basic pizza, plus $1 for every topping that is ordered.

1. a. Fill in the table showing the number of toppings t and the cost of the pizza c.

Toppings t	Cost c	(t, c)
0		
1		
2		
3		
4		
5		

b. Graph the ordered pairs (t, c) on the grid below.

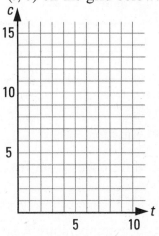

c. Write an equation that represents c in terms of t. _____

d. What would be a suitable domain for this graph? _____

In 2 and 3, Pat's plans for increasing her profit are given. For each plan, fill in the table, make a graph, and write an equation for the graph. Then describe how the graph is different from the first graph.

2. Plan A: Raise the basic pizza charge to $8, but continue to charge $1 for each topping.

Toppings t	Cost c	(t, c)
0		
1		
2		
3		
4		
5		

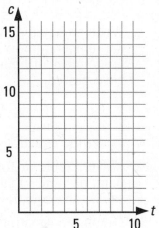

equation: _____

differences from first graph: _____

_____

3. Plan B: Keep the basic charge at $6, but charge $1.50 for each topping.

Toppings *t*	Cost *c*	(*t, c*)
0		
1		
2		
3		
4		
5		

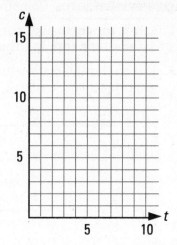

equation: _____

differences from first graph: _____

_____

4. The temperature was -1°, but it was dropping 3° each hour.

a. Complete the table.

Hours *h*	Temperature *t*
0	
1	
2	
3	

b. Graph the situation below.

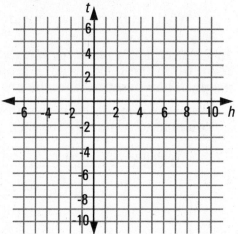

c. Write an equation to describe the temperature in terms of the number of hours that have passed.

_____

5. Consider the equation $y = -2x + 7$.

a. Make a table of four pairs of values that satisfy the equation.

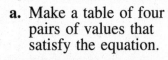

b. Graph the equation at the right.

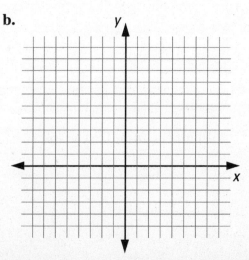

LESSON MASTER **5-1 A**

Questions on SPUR Objectives
See pages 343-346 for objectives.

Representations Objective H

In 1 and 2, an equation is given, a. Give the coordinates of three points that satisfy the equation. b. Graph the equation.

1. $x = -3$

2. $y = 5$

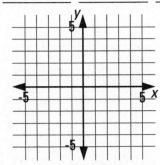
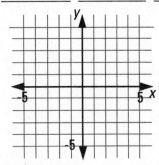

In 3–5, graph the given line and the point (2, 5). Tell where (2, 5) lies in relation to the line: *on, above, below, to the left,* or *to the right*.

3. $y = -1$

4. $x = 2$

5. $x = 5$

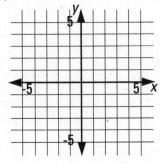
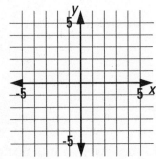
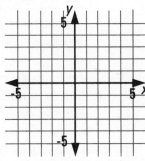

In 6–10, give an equation for the line shown or described.

6.

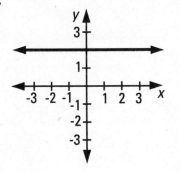

7.

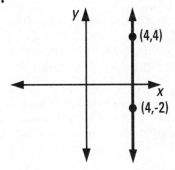

► **LESSON MASTER 5-1 A** *page 2*

8. the vertical line through (-5, 1) _____

9. the horizontal line through (0, -8) _____

10. the line through (-3, 5), (0, -5), and $\left(\frac{1}{3}, -5\right)$ _____

Representations Objective I

---

11. The Gomez family has bought a collie
   puppy which weighs 23 pounds. The
   puppy is expected to gain 2 pounds per
   week. Full-grown collies typically
   weight about 65 pounds.

   a. Write an equation to describe the
      puppy's weight *y* after *x* weeks.

      _____

   b. Graph your equation from Part a
      on the grid at the right.

   c. Graph *y* = 65 to represent the final
      expected weight of the puppy on the
      grid at the right.

   d. Use the graph to approximate when
      the puppy will weigh 65 pounds.

      _____

   e. Check your answer to Part d by
      solving an equation.   _____

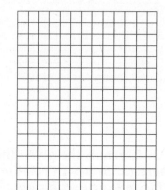

**In 12–14, use this information: Megan has decided to start
lifting weights. Now she can curl 10 pounds and she feels
she can increase this by 2.5 pounds each month if she works
out regularly. This is shown on the graph below.**

12. Draw a horizontal line showing
    where the weight is 17.5 pounds.

13. Write an inequality to describe
    the number of months *x*
    during which Megan can curl
    no more than 17.5 pounds.   _____

14. Write an inequality to describe
    when she can curl more than
    15 pounds.   _____

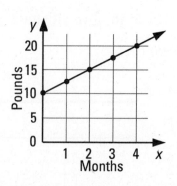

LESSON MASTER 5-2 A

Representations Objective G

1. In the week before the election for mayor, the voters who had been undecided were finally choosing between the two candidates. According to poll results, Schultz, who started the week with 47,000 votes, began gaining 450 votes each day. Chen, who started with 44,900, began gaining 800 votes a day.

DAY	SCHULTZ	CHEN
1	47,000	44,900
2		
3		
4		
5		
6		
7		
Elec. Day		

   a. Fill in the chart at the right.

   b. Who should be expected to win the election?

   _____

   c. Write an equation for Schultz's votes S in terms of the day number d. _____

   d. Write an equation for Chen's votes C in terms of the day number d. _____

   e. What equation could be solved to estimate when the two candidates were tied? _____

2. Yuriko has been offered two jobs. Mendoza, Inc., pays $25,000 per year at first, but each year she will get an $800 raise. Consolidated Industries pays $28,000 now, but yearly raises are only $300. Yuriko made a spreadsheet to help her choose between the two jobs.

   a. What formula could be used in cell C3?

   _____

   b. What formula could be used in cell C4?

   _____

   c. Complete the spreadsheet.

   d. How does the pay for the jobs compare over a 10-year period?

	A	B	C
1	YEAR	MENDOZA	CONSOLIDATED
2	1	25,000	28,000
3	2		
4	3		
5	4		
6	5		
7	6		
8	7		
9	8		
10	9		
11	10		

   _____

   _____

   _____

   _____

LESSON MASTER 5-3 A

Skills Objective A

1.

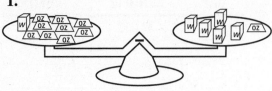

a. Write the equation represented by this drawing.

_____

b. Solve the equation to find the weight w of one box.

_____

In 2–7, solve each equation and check the result.

2. $x + 50 = 2x + 100$ 3. $9n = 4n - 35$ 4. $1.2 - .4y = .6y + 4.2$

5. $3(2x + 4) + 2 = 4x + 50$ 6. $C = \frac{9}{5}C + 32$ 7. $4(6 - 3y) = 2(15y + 12)$

Properties Objective E

In 8 and 9, tell what should be done to both sides of the equation first in order to solve.

8. $13x + 5 = -9x - 1$ 9. $5y + 3 = 13y$

_____   _____

Uses Objective F

---

11. A club sponsored a concert. The income from the concert came from a $250 donation by the school activity fund and ticket sales at $8 per ticket. Rent for an auditorium was $200. The band was paid $1400 plus $2 for each ticket sold. Since the income was exactly equal to expenses, the club just broke even and did not make money. Let x = the number of tickets sold.

a. Write an expression for the income. _____

b. Write an expression for the expenses. _____

c. Write an equation that says the income and expenses were equal. _____

d. How many tickets were sold? _____

Name _____

LESSON MASTER 5-4 A

Questions on SPUR Objectives
See pages 343-346 for objectives.

Uses   Objective F
Representations Objective I

---

1. The graph below shows estimated populations of two towns in t years.

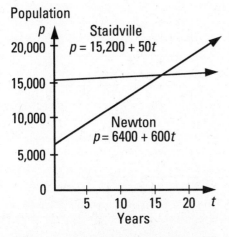

a. Use an equation to estimate in how many years the populations will be equal. Use the graph to check your answer.

_____

b. For what values of t is Newton's estimated population less?

_____

c. When is Newton's estimated population greater?

_____

2. A gas station that normally sells gasoline for $1.29 per gallon is offering the special deal advertised at the right. Let g = gallons of gas purchased and c = cost.

a. Write an equation describing the cost of g gallons at the regular price.

_____

b. Write an equation describing the cost of g gallons with a car wash.

_____

c. Graph the two equations from Parts **a** and **b**.

d. Use your graph to tell when the cost is the same with or without a car wash.

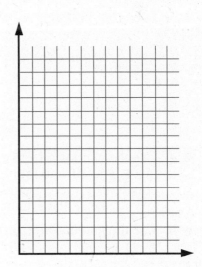

_____

e. What equation could be used to answer the question in Part **d**?

_____

f. Karen needs 10 gallons of gas. Is it cheaper to get her car washed also?

_____

51

LESSON MASTER

5-5
A

Representations Objective J

In 1–3, use the window at the right.

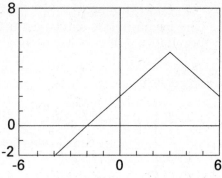

1. Write two inequalities for the window.

_____

2. As you move from $x = -4$ to $x = 1$, what happens to the height of the graph?

_____

3. What are the coordinates of the point where the graph crosses the y-axis?

_____

4. What are the coordinates of the highest point on the graph?

_____

5. Describe a window that would show the highest point in the center of the screen.

_____

In 6 and 7, graph $y = x^2 - 4x - 21$ on an automatic grapher, using the given window. Sketch the graph, being sure to show the limits of the window and the axes, if they appear.

6. window: $-5 \leq x \leq 5$; $-5 \leq y \leq 5$ 7. window: $0 \leq x \leq 30$; $-10 \leq y \leq 10$

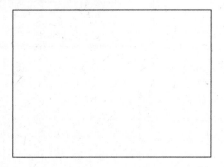   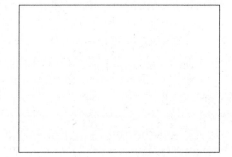

8. **a.** Use the window $-15 \leq x \leq 15$, $-10 \leq y \leq 10$, and graph the two equations $y = 3 - x$ and $y = x - 3$. Sketch the graphs at the right.

  b. Use the graph to find a value of x for which $x - 3 \neq 3 - x$.

  _____

  c. Use the graph to find a value of x for which $x - 3 = 3 - x$.

  _____

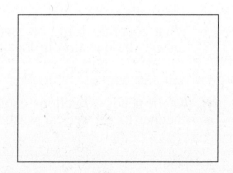

LESSON MASTER **5-6 A**

Skills Objective B

1. Write an inequality to find the values of x that make $10x - 12$ greater than $4x + 42$. _____

In 2–7 solve and check.

2. $-2y - 10 > 3y + 5$

3. $12y + 3 + 4y \geq 2(7y + 1)$

4. $8y < 10y - 30$

5. $-4.8m - 3 > 10 - 5.2m$

6. $4(2n - 1) \leq 4(n - 1)$

7. $(20x + 180) - (30x + 50) < 40x - 60$

Properties Objective E

9. Show your work as you solve $4x - 8 < 9 - 2x$

   a. by adding $-4x$ to both sides.　　**b.** by adding $2x$ to both sides.

   c. Which method is easier? Explain why.

   _____

   _____

Uses Objective F

10. A mail-order club sells CDs for $10.99 each, but charges $10 to join. Sarah pays $13.99 for a CD in a store.

    a. If Sarah buys 20 CDs, is her total cost less in a store or through the club? _____

    b. What is the maximum number of CDs for which the store is less expensive? _____

    c. If the club charges an additional $2 per CD for shipping, what is the maximum number of CDs for which the store is less expensive? _____

LESSON MASTER **5-7 A**

Skills Objective D

In 1–8, solve the formula for the given variable.

1. $K = C + 273$ for C **2.** $m = 12y$ for y **3.** $p = 2a + b$ for a

4. $V = \frac{1}{3}Bh$ for h **5.** $p = 2(\ell + w)$ for ℓ **6.** $C = \frac{3}{10}S$ for S

7. $C = 180 - A - B$ for A **8.** $s = \frac{n}{2}(f + \ell)$ for ℓ

9. The formula $C = p\left(\frac{\ell w}{9}\right)$ gives the cost C of carpeting a room ℓ feet long and w feet wide, where p = price per square yard of the carpeting. Solve $C = p\left(\frac{\ell w}{9}\right)$ for ℓ. _____

In 10–13, solve the equation for y.

10. $5x + y = 35$ **11.** $-6 = x - y$

12. $20 = -12x + 4y$ **13.** $3x - 3y = 15$

Properties Objective E

14. Solve the equation $7m + 5 = 3m - 7$ by first adding

   a. $-7m$ to both sides.   **b.** $-3m$ to both sides.

   _____   _____

   c. How are your solutions related?

   _____

LESSON MASTER

5-8
A

Questions on SPUR Objectives
See pages 343-346 for objectives.

Skills Objective A

In 1–4, solve the equation.

1. $\dfrac{5n}{6} + 3 = 10$

2. $\dfrac{7}{8} = \dfrac{4}{3} - \dfrac{1}{4}a$

3. $4x + .02 = 1.5x + 9$

4. $\dfrac{2}{3}\left(2x + \dfrac{1}{2}\right) = \dfrac{2}{3}x - 8$

Skills Objective B

In 5–8, solve the inequality.

5. $\dfrac{-x}{4} + \dfrac{5}{6} < \dfrac{4x}{3} + 2$

6. $700y + 200 \geq 1100 - 100y$

7. $-\dfrac{n}{5} + 6 > n$

8. $\dfrac{1}{10}a + \dfrac{1}{2}a + \dfrac{3}{8} \leq 1$

Properties Objective E

**In 9 and 10, write the equation that results when
you multiply through by the given number.**

9. In $\dfrac{4}{9}n + \dfrac{1}{3} = 5$, multiply both sides by 9. _____

10. In $8x + \dfrac{3}{5} = \dfrac{x}{2} - \dfrac{7}{4}$, multiply both sides by 20. _____

11. Jenny and Pedro disagree about how to solve $\dfrac{3}{10}x + 4 = \dfrac{5}{6}$.
    Jenny says to multiply by 60 and Pedro says to multiply by 30.
    Which way is better? Why?

_____

_____

12. Tell what to multiply each side by to make the sentence easier to solve.

a. $4{,}000m + 10{,}000 < 168{,}000$ _____

b. $.4m + 1 < 16.8$ _____

13. Fill in the blank with a property or an operation with a given number to explain the step taken to solve $t = a + (n - 1)d$ for n.

$t = a + (n - 1)d$

$t = a + nd - d$ _____ Property

$t - a = nd - d$ _____ to each side.

$t - a + d = nd$ _____ to each side.

$\dfrac{1}{d}(t - a + d) = n$ _____ each side by _____.

Uses Objective F

14. Of the money that an emergency-relief organization spent last year, $\frac{3}{5}$ was for emergency food and $\frac{1}{4}$ was for emergency shelter. The rest, which came to $400,000, was used for expenses.

a. Write an equation to describe this situation. _____

b. How much did the organization spend last year? _____

c. Check your answer to Part **b** by finding the total amount of money used for food and shelters. _____

15. A baseball team is raising money by selling magazine subscriptions. Donato accounted for $\frac{1}{4}$ of the team's sales and Marty made $\frac{1}{8}$. Together they sold 48 subscriptions. How many did the team sell altogether? _____

LESSON MASTER

5-9
A

Skills Objective C

1. If $11x = 6$, find the value of $33x + 50$. _____

2. If $2n = 4.1$, find the value of $12n + 1$. _____

3. If $15x + 3 = 297$, find the value of $15x + 4$. _____

4. If $5.2y - 16.9 = 85.2$, find the value
   of $10(5.2y - 16.9)$. _____

In 6–13, use chunking to simplify the expression.

6. $6(5y + 2) + 4(5y + 2)$

7. $-8(x^2 + 3) + 5(x^2 + 3) - 9(x^2 + 3)$

_____

8. $\dfrac{3}{2x + 5} + \dfrac{9}{2x + 5}$

9. $\dfrac{12y}{x^2 - 11} - \dfrac{2y}{x^2 - 11}$

_____

10. $\dfrac{x + 9}{6} \cdot \dfrac{15}{x + 9}$

11. $\dfrac{18}{5(x - 1)} \cdot \dfrac{2(x - 1)}{11}$

_____

12. $8\sqrt{13} + 9\sqrt{13}$

13. $10\sqrt{2} - \sqrt{2}$

_____

In 14–17, solve the equation.

14. $(y - 1)^2 = 49$

15. $(x + 8)^2 = 1$

16. $(2n + 10)^2 = 144$

17. $(5x)^2 = 900$

18. If $\sqrt{x + 5} = 64$, what is the value

   a. of $x + 5$? _____

   b. of x? _____

LESSON MASTER

6-1
A

Skills Objective A

In 1–6, fill in the blanks.

1. $\frac{2}{n}$ = _____ ÷ _____

2. $\frac{5n}{8}$ = $5n \cdot$ _____

3. $\dfrac{\frac{3n}{a}}{\frac{5x}{w}}$ = _____ ÷ _____

4. $\frac{5}{n} \div \frac{x+6}{a}$ = _____ · _____

5. $\frac{1}{n} \div -48 = \frac{1}{n} \cdot$ _____

6. $\dfrac{x}{\frac{a}{b}}$ = _____ · _____

In 7–14, simplify.

7. $\frac{2n}{5} \div \frac{n}{10}$ _____

8. $\frac{-5}{n} \div 2x$ _____

9. $\dfrac{\frac{2}{5}}{\frac{7}{8}}$ _____

10. $\dfrac{-\frac{n}{12}}{-\frac{n}{30}}$ _____

11. $\frac{a}{4x} \div \frac{ax}{5}$ _____

12. $\dfrac{\frac{5x}{15}}{x}$ _____

13. $\dfrac{\frac{1}{n}}{n}$ _____

14. $\dfrac{3\frac{1}{2}}{-\frac{4}{7}}$ _____

Name _____

LESSON MASTER 6-2 A

Uses Objective E

1. The world's first steam-powered railroad trip took place in England in 1804. The trip took 4 hours and covered a distance of $9\frac{1}{2}$ miles.

   a. What was the train's average speed in miles per hour?

   b. How long did it take the train to travel one mile?

   _____ _____

In 2–7, give a rate for each situation.

2. The divers dove 300 meters in 45 seconds. _____

3. The divers rose 15 m to the surface in 2 min. _____

4. Today $2\frac{1}{2}$ inches of rain fell in 2 hours. _____

5. A 6-oz steak contains about 660 calories. _____

6. The Lees' car traveled 450 miles on 17.6 gallons of gasoline. _____

7. In 1790, the first U.S. Census reported that the area of the U.S. was 864,746 square miles and the population was 3,929,214. _____

8. A grocery store sells a 48-oz bottle of apple juice for $1.50 and a 36-oz bottle for $1.19. Find the unit cost (cost per ounce) of the

   a. larger bottle. _____ b. smaller bottle. _____

   c. Which is the better buy? _____

In 9–11 give the density of each item (weight per volume).

ITEM	WEIGHT	VOLUME	DENSITY
9. egg	62 grams	50 cubic centimeters	
10. onion	105 grams	100 cubic centimeters	
11. banana	180 grams	190 cubic centimeters	

12. Which is faster, running $3x$ laps in $2m$ minutes or $5x$ laps in $3m$ minutes? Explain your answer.

_____

_____

59

LESSON MASTER

6-3
A

Uses Objectives F and H

1. In the 1992 men's national weightlifting championships, Brian Okala, in the 52-kg class, lifted 87.5 kg. Rick Schultz, in the 110-kg class, lifted 162.5 kg. Who lifted more in relation to his body weight?

   _____

2. Maria's special sauce for vegetables is made of 5 parts mayonnaise, 2 parts mustard, and 1 part lemon juice. How much of each ingredient should she use to make 2 cups of the sauce?

   _____   _____   _____

   　　mayonnaise　　　　　　　mustard　　　　　　　lemon juice

3. In his major-league career, Babe Ruth had 2,873 hits in 8,399 times at bat. What was his lifetime batting average? (*Batting average* is the ratio of hits to times at bat, expressed as a decimal rounded to the nearest thousandth.)

   _____

4. According to the census, the 1990 U.S. population was about 248,710,000. California had about 29,760,000 residents and Montana had about 799,000. Find the percent of the U.S. population that lived

   a. in California.　　　　　　　　　_____

   b. in Montana.　　　　　　　　　　_____

5. A tent originally costing $125.95 is on sale for $107.60. After tax is added, the price is $114.06.

   a. What is the percent of discount?　　_____

   b. What is the percent of tax?　　　　　_____

6. Companies keep statistics on different TV shows to judge which are the most popular and to determine advertising fees. A show's *rating* is the percent of households with TVs that watch the show. A show's *share* is the percent of households with the TV *on* that watch the show. Suppose a city has 2,000,000 households with TV and at 10 P.M. 830,000 are watching TV. Of those 90,000 are watching the Channel 3 News.

   a. Give the rating. _____　b. Give the share. _____

   c. A very popular show could have a rating of 25%. How many people in this city can be expected to watch such a show?　　_____

LESSON MASTER

6-4
A

Questions on SPUR Objectives
See pages 412-415 for objectives.

Uses Objective G

1. A survey asked people to name their favorite sport. Give the relative frequency as a fraction of people who like baseball best if

   a. 385 people were polled and 315 did *not* pick baseball.

   b. 209 people were polled and 150 did *not* pick baseball.

   _____

   _____

   c. 950 people were polled and *x* did *not* pick baseball.

   d. *p* people were polled and *n* did *not* pick baseball.

   _____

   _____

2. As of May, 1992, of about 92,000,000 U.S. households that had TVs, there were close to 56,000,000 that had cable TV. Estimate the relative frequency of households with TVs that

   a. also had cable. _____

   b. did not have cable. _____

3. A charity sold 418 raffle tickets. One ticket will be drawn and the ticket-holder will receive a new bicycle. Hojung bought 5 tickets. Let the event E = Hojung wins and S = set of all outcomes. Find

   a. $N(E)$, _____

   b. $N(S)$, _____

   c. $P(E)$, _____

   d. P(Hojung does not win). _____

In 4–6 a card is drawn from a regular deck. Find

4. P(queen). _____

5. P(jack, queen, or king). _____

6. P(queen of hearts). _____

7. Lucy fills a pot with a mixture of 1200 black beans and 300 white beans, all the same size. When she grabs a handful of 15 beans, she finds that 10 are black.

   a. What is the probability of choosing a white bean? _____

   b. What is Lucy's relative frequency of choosing a white bean? _____

   c. Why do the answers to Parts **a** and **b** do not have to be the same?

   _____

   _____

   _____

LESSON MASTER

6-5 A

Skills Objective B

1. 15 out of 180 is what percent?

_____

2. 4.8 is what percent of 6.2?

_____

3. What is 2% of 497?

_____

4. What is 6.8% of 500?

_____

5. What is 28% of $36,000?

_____

6. 85% of what number is 119?

_____

7. 40% of a number is 73. What is the number?

_____

8. 5% of a number is 635. What is the number?

_____

Uses Objective H

9. School health records show that 70% of the children have been immunized against polio. If the school has 350 children, how many have had a polio immunization?

_____

10. A headline reads: ACME, INC., LAYS OFF 15% OF WORK FORCE
2500 People to Lose Jobs

How many workers did Acme employ before the layoff?

_____

11. In 1990, about 79.3% of the U.S. population lived in metropolitan areas. The U.S. population was about 249 million people. How many lived

a. in metropolitan areas?

_____

b. outside metropolitan areas?

_____

12. After 6% sales tax was added, a T-shirt cost $9.53. Find the cost of the T-shirt without tax.

_____

13. A sweater is on sale for 30% off. The sale price is $22.40. What is the regular price?

_____

14. A marine biologist found that there are about 20% more of a certain type of fish in the area in summer than in winter. She estimated that in the summer there are 1500 of these fish in the bay. How many are there in winter?

_____

LESSON MASTER

6-6 A

Representations Objective J

1. In a 40-ft-by-100-ft field is a dog on a 12-foot chain. If some children hit a softball into the field, what is the probability that the ball will land within reach of the dog?

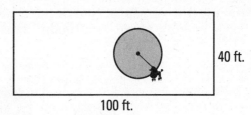

40 ft.

100 ft.

_____

2. This target is made of circles with radii of 10, 15, and 20 inches.

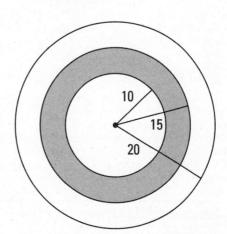

   a. Find the area of each circle.

   _____

   b. Find the area of the shaded region.

   _____

   c. If a dart is thrown at random, what is the probability that it will land in the shaded ring?

   _____

   d. What is the probability that it will land in the outermost ring? _____

3.

   A B

   |——————————••———————————————|

   2 miles $\frac{1}{4}$ mile $3\frac{1}{4}$ miles

   Ben plans to march in a parade in Washington, D.C., which will go past a reviewing stand where the President will sit to watch. The parade route is shown. The portion between *A* and *B* is in view of the reviewing stand. If Ben trips at a random point along the route, what is the probability that the President might see him trip? _____

For 4 and 5, give the probability that the spinner will land in region A.

4.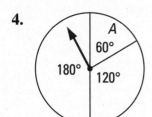

5.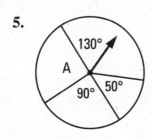

_____   _____

LESSON MASTER **6-7 A**

Uses Objective H

In 1–3, Mayuko enlarged a picture (A) on a photocopy machine by a factor of 130%. She decided the result (B) wasn't quite large enough so she enlarged it again by a factor of 110% (C).

A   B   C

Find the height of the other two pictures if the height of

1. picture A is 10 in.

B _____

C _____

2. picture B is 10 in.

A _____

C _____

3. picture C is 24 in.

A _____

B _____

Representations Objective K

4. a. Graph quadrilateral *ABCD* if $A = (4, -2)$, $B = (2, 0)$, $C = (5, 4)$ and $D = (4, 0)$.

b. Graph the image $A'B'C'D'$ under a size change of magnitude 2.

c. Graph $A''B''C''D''$, the image of *ABCD*, under a size change of magnitude $-\frac{1}{2}$.

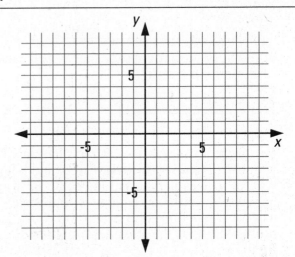

5. A figure undergoes a size change under the rule that the image of (x, y) is $(5x, 5y)$. How does this affect the figure's size?

_____

In 6–8, the magnitude of a size change is given. Tell if it is an *expansion*, a *contraction*, or *neither*.

6. $k = \frac{2}{3}$ **7.** $k = -10$ **8.** $k = 1$

_____   _____   _____

LESSON MASTER 6-8 A

Skills Objective C

In 1–6, use the Means-Extremes Property to solve.

1. $\dfrac{7}{8} = \dfrac{x}{4}$

2. $\dfrac{5a}{3} = \dfrac{15}{2}$

3. $\dfrac{18}{w + 8} = \dfrac{2}{3}$

4. $\dfrac{2x + 1}{3} = \dfrac{5x - 5}{6}$

5. $\dfrac{v + 5}{v + 7} = \text{-}8$

6. $\dfrac{2}{w} = \dfrac{w}{18}$

In 7 and 8, a. give the exact solutions, and
b. give the solutions rounded to the nearest hundredth.

7. $\dfrac{x}{3} = \dfrac{1}{x}$

8. $\dfrac{5}{2y} = \dfrac{y}{6}$

 a. _____

 b. _____

 a. _____

 b. _____

Properties Objective D

9. Explain how you can use the Means-Extremes Property to determine if the fractions $\dfrac{3}{5}$ and $\dfrac{7.5}{12.5}$ are equal.

_____

_____

Uses Objective I

10. In 1990, 39.5 million foreigners visited the U.S. Of these, 17.3 million were from Canada. If the total number of visitors increases to 50 million in the year 2000, how many can be expected to be from Canada? _____

11. Carlo figures that when he is driving at highway speed his car's engine turns at a rate of 3000 revolutions per minute. He has also found that when the engine turns 7 times, the wheels turn 2 times. If Carlo drives for 1 hour,

 a. how many times does the engine turn? _____

 b. how many times does a wheel turn? _____

12. On the 10 o'clock news, the sportscaster can cover 10 sports stories in 3 minutes 45 seconds. If his time slot is increased to 5 minutes, how many stories can he cover? _____

LESSON MASTER

6-9 A

Questions on SPUR Objectives
See pages 412-415 for objectives.

Representations Objective L

1. Two common sizes for photographs are 5 in. by 7 in. and 8 in. by 10 in.

7 in.

10 in.

5 in.

8 in.

   a. What is the ratio of the widths of the pictures? _____

   b. What is the ratio of the lengths of the pictures? _____

   c. Are the pictures similar? Explain why or why not.

_____

_____

2. Triangle CAT is similar to triangle DOG.

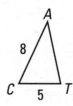
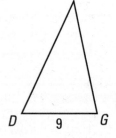

8

C 5 T

D 9 G

   a. Calculate $\dfrac{CT}{DG}$. _____

   b. Find two ratios of sides equal to $\dfrac{CT}{DG}$.

   _____   _____

   c. What side of $\triangle DOG$ corresponds to $\overline{CA}$ in $\triangle CAT$? _____

   d. Write a proportion to find the length of $\overline{DO}$. _____

In 3–5, the two trapezoids are similar. Find the length of

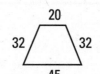
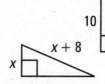

20

32   32

45

50

A B

D C

3. $\overline{AB}$. _____

4. $\overline{BC}$. _____

5. $\overline{DC}$. _____

6. These triangles are similar.

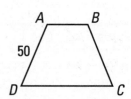
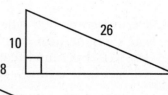

10

26

x + 8

x

   a. Find x and $x + 8$.

   _____

   b. Find the length of the third side of each triangle. (Hint: Do not use a proportion.) _____

   c. Give two possible ratios of similitude. _____

LESSON MASTER 7-1 A

Uses Objective E

In 1–5, use the chart below. It shows the number
to the nearest million of U.S. households with
cable TV every five years from 1970 to 1990.

Year	1970	1975	1980	1985	1990
Households	4 million	9 million	15 million	36 million	55 million

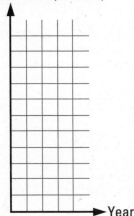

Households (millions)

Year

1. Graph the information on the grid at the left.
   Connect the points.

2. Which segment is steeper, the one connecting
   (1975, 9 million) to (1980, 15 million)
   or the one connecting (1980, 15 million)
   to (1985, 36 million)?

   _____

3. What was the rate of change of number of
   households with cable from 1970 to 1975?

   _____

4. What was the rate of change of the number of
   households with cable from 1985 to 1990?

   _____

5. For the years shown, was the rate of
   change ever negative?

   _____

In 6 and 7, use the table at the right.
It shows the prices a vacation resort
charges for stays of the given durations.

Days	Cost
3	$289
4	$359
7	$449

6. a. What is the rate of change from a
   4-day vacation to a 7-day vacation?

   _____

   b. What is the unit of the rate of change?

   _____

7. Is the rate of change from 3 to 4 days the
   same as the rate of change from 4 days to
   7 days?

   _____

In 8–12, use the graph below. It shows the height of
Greg's feet as he dives off the high board.

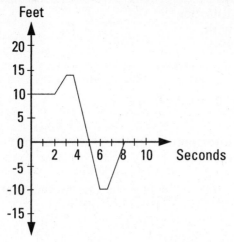

8. How many seconds pass before
Greg's feet leave the board?

_____

9. How long is he in the air?

_____

10. About how high does he jump?

_____

_____

11. What is happening between 5 and 6 seconds?

_____

12. How high is the diving board? _____

In 13–14, use this spreadsheet. It shows the average
number of pounds of plastic each person in the U.S.
discards each year, projected through the year 2000.

	A	B	C
1	YEAR	POUNDS	RATE OF CHANGE IN POUNDS/YEAR DURING PREVIOUS DECADE
2	1960	3.7	
3	1970	29.2	2.55
4	1980	69.4	4.02
5	1990	116.8	
6	2000	157.0	

13. What formula could be in cell C5? _____

14. Complete the spreadsheet.

LESSON MASTER 7-2 A

Skills Objective A

In 1 and 2, calculate the slope of the line through the two points.

1. (3, 20) and (7, 36) _____

2. (-6, 5) and (10, 9) _____

In 3 and 4, find the slope of the line.

3. _____

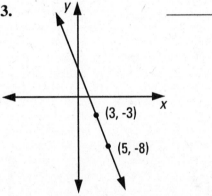

4. _____

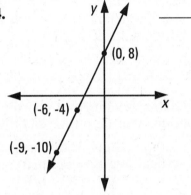

5. The points (1, 8) and (m, 14) are on a line with slope 3. Find the value of m. _____

Properties Objective D

6. If a line passes through the points (a, b) and (j, k), what is its slope? _____

7. Explain how to tell if the slope of a line is positive, negative, or zero by looking at its graph.

_____

_____

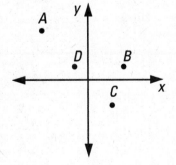

For 8–10, use the graph at the left.

8. Name two points on a line with positive slope. _____

9. Name two points on a line with zero slope. _____

10. The slope determined by points A and D seems equal to the slope determined by which two points?

_____

LESSON MASTER 7-3 A

Properties Objective D

1. Fill in the blanks. If the slope of a line is -4, then as you go

   _____unit(s) to the right you go _____ unit(s) _____ .

2. **a.** Give an example of coordinates of two
   points that lie on the same horizontal line. _____

   b. Use the points from Part **a** to explain why the slope of a
   horizontal line is zero.

   _____

3. **a.** Give an example of coordinates of two
   points that lie on the same vertical line. _____

   b. Use the points from Part **a** to explain why the slope of a
   vertical line is undefined.

   _____

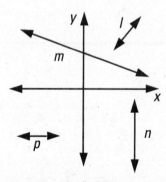

**In 4–7, tell which line has the
given slope.**

4. 0 _____

5. negative _____

6. positive _____

7. undefined _____

**In 8–10, consider the line which goes through the point
(10, -2) and has the indicated slope. Name another point
with integer coordinates that lies on the line.**

8. 3 _____   **9.** -1 _____   **10.** $\frac{1}{2}$ _____

Uses Objective E

11. In order for the Wassermans to install their new washing
    machine, they had to move the old machine out of their
    basement. To do this, they built a small ramp by laying a
    piece of plywood over the 5 steps leading to the outside.
    If the rise (the vertical part) of each step was 6 inches and
    the run (the horizontal part) of each step was 9 inches,
    what was the slope of the ramp? _____

▶ **LESSON MASTER 7-3 A** *page 2*

Representations Objective H

In 12 and 13, graph the line described.

12. Passes through (-1, 4) and has slope -2

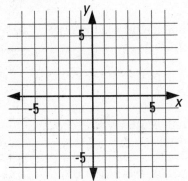

13. Passes through (0, 2) and has slope $\frac{2}{3}$

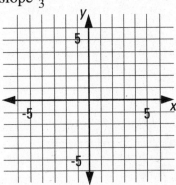

14.

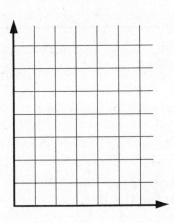

A long-distance call from Midland to Valleyhill costs $.50 for the first minute, plus $.30 for each additional minute.

a. Give the coordinates of four points showing (duration of call, cost).

_____ _____

_____ _____

b. Draw a graph showing how the cost changes as the minutes increase.

15.

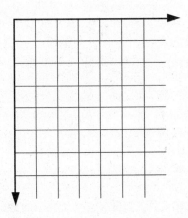

Two minutes after diving from the surface of the ocean, a submarine was 100 m below the surface. Then it descended 15 m every minute.

a. Write the coordinates of four points showing (minutes, position of submarine).

_____ _____

_____ _____

b. Draw a graph showing how the sub's position changed over time.

LESSON MASTER

7-4
A

Questions on SPUR Objectives
See pages 480-483 for objectives.

Vocabulary

1. Write the *slope-intercept form* of the equation of a line. _____

In 2–5, use the graph below.

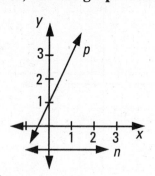

2. What is the *y-intercept* of line *p*? _____

3. What is the *slope* of line *p*? _____

4. What is the *y-intercept* of line *n*? _____

5. What is the *slope* of line *n*? _____

Skills Objective B

In 6 and 7, a line is described. Write its equation in slope-intercept form.

6. slope $\frac{2}{3}$, *y*-intercept 4

7. slope -5, *y*-intercept 0

_____   _____

**In 8 and 9, a line is graphed. a. Give the slope of the line
b. Give the *y*-intercept. c. Write an equation for the line.**

8.

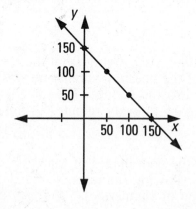

9.

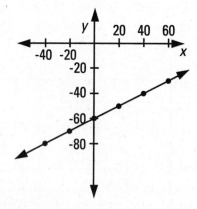

a. _____   a. _____

b. _____   b. _____

c. _____   c. _____

▶ **LESSON MASTER 7-4 A** *page 2*

Skills Objective C

In 10 and 11, an equation of a line is given.
a. Change the equation to slope-intercept form.
b. Give the slope. c. Give the y-intercept.

10. $4x + 5y = 15$ **a.** _____   **b.** _____   **c.** _____

11. $x - y = -3$ **a.** _____   **b.** _____   **c.** _____

Uses Objective F

12. The basic fee for repairing a piece of machinery is $75 plus $20 for each hour of labor. If this were described by a graph, give the

    a. y-intercept.   _____   **b.** slope.   _____

13. The price of a cheese pizza is $4.50 with a charge of $0.50 for each additional topping. If this situation were graphed with x = number of toppings and y = total price, give the

    a. y-intercept.   _____   **b.** slope.   _____

    c. equation.   _____

Representations Objective H

In 14 and 15, graph the line.

14. slope -3, y-intercept 5

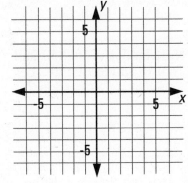

15. $-2x + y = 1$

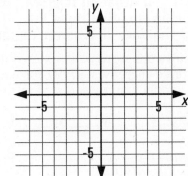

LESSON MASTER

7-5
A

Skills Objective B

In 1–4, a point and slope are given. Write an equation
for the line with that slope that passes through the point.

1. slope 5, point (2, -1) _____

2. slope -3, point (-6, 0) _____

3. slope $\frac{1}{4}$, point (-1, -8) _____

4. slope $-\frac{2}{5}$, point (6, 4) _____

5.

   a. Write an equation
      for the line graphed
      at the left. _____

   b. What are the
      coordinates of
      point T? _____

   c. Show that the coordinates of point T
      satisfy your equation from Part **a**.

      _____

   d. At what point will the line cross the y-axis? _____

Uses Objective F

In 6 and 7, a situation is given. **a.** Give a possible point (x, y).
b. Write an equation for a line which relates x and y. **c.** Find the
slope of the line. **d.** Answer the question.

6. A hardware store sells extension ladders. A 16-ft ladder costs $50 and
the price increases $7.50 for each additional foot of ladder length. Let
x = ladder length and y = price. What is the cost of a 28-ft ladder?

   a. _____   b. _____

   c. _____   d. _____

7. Felicita's Fashions is having a sale on dresses. By the 8th day of the sale,
there were 130 dresses left. The store sells about 25 dresses each day.
Let x = the number of days since the sale started and y = the number
of dresses left. How many days will it take to sell all the dresses?

   a. _____   b. _____

   c. _____   d. _____

LESSON MASTER **7-6 A**

Skills Objective B

In 1–4, write the equation in slope-intercept
form of the line containing the two points.

1. (1, 5) and (3, 14)

2. (-2, -4) and (3, 16)

_____

3. (6, 0) and (11, -5)

4. (12, 18) and (3, 12)

_____

5. a. Give an equation for the line that
contains (3, 2) and (5, -2).

_____

b. Check your answer by graphing
the line on the grid at the right.

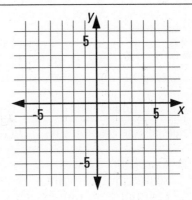

Uses Objective F

In 6 and 7, a situation is described. **a.** Give two ordered
pairs for the situation. **b.** Write an equation for the line
through the two points. **c.** Answer the question.

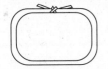

6. A loop of string is formed into a rectangle. If the width
of the rectangle is 12 inches, the height is 6 inches. If
the width is 10 inches, the height is 8 inches. Let w =
width and h = height. If the width is 15 inches, what is
the height?

a. _____   **b.** _____

c. _____

7. When the Gonzalez family's new kitten was 6 weeks old it weighed
8 ounces. When it was 10 weeks old it weighed 10 ounces. Let
x = the age of the kitten and y = the weight of the kitten. If the
kitten's weight gain had been linear, how much did it weigh at birth?

a. _____   **b.** _____

c. _____

LESSON MASTER 7-7 A

Uses Objective G

1. a. On the first grid make a scatterplot that is approximately linear.

b. On the second grid make a scatterplot that is *not* approximately linear.

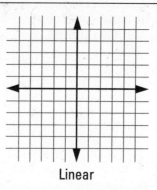

Linear

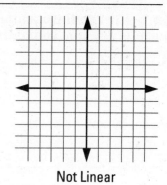

Not Linear

2. The table below was developed by a French veterinarian, Dr. A. LeBeau. It gives the age of a cat or dog and its corresponding age in human years.

Cat/Dog Age (years)	0.5	1	2	4	6	8	10	14	18	21
Human Age (years)	10	15	24	32	40	48	56	72	91	106

a. Carefully draw a scatterplot of points (animal age, human age).

b. Fit a line to the data by eye and draw it with a ruler.

c. Give the coordinates of two points that lie on the line you drew.

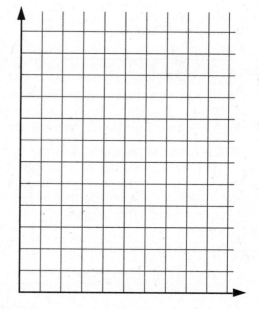

_____

d. Use your two points to find an equation for your line.

_____

e. According to your equation, what happens to the corresponding human age as the cat or dog ages one year?

f. Use your equation to find the approximate human age equivalent to that of a 15-year-old dog. _____

LESSON MASTER 7-8 A

Skills Objective C

In 1 and 2, tell if the equation is in standard form.

1. $y = 3x - 5$ _____ **2.** $4x + 2y = 18$ _____

In 3–6, an equation is given. **a.** Rewrite the equation in standard form with integer coefficients. **b.** Give the values of A, B, and C.

3. $y = -4x - 6$ **a.** _____   **b.** _____

4. $y = \frac{2}{3}x + 7$ **a.** _____   **b.** _____

5. $y = -\frac{1}{5}x + \frac{1}{3}$ **a.** _____   **b.** _____

6. $y - x = 16$ **a.** _____   **b.** _____

Uses Objective F

7. In a basketball-shooting game you get points in two ways: 10 points if you hit the rim and 50 points if you get a basket. Marcos hit the rim x times and got y baskets. His final score was 200.

  a. Write an equation in standard form that describes the relationship between x and y. _____

  b. Give three solutions to your equation in Part **a**. _____

Representations Objective H

In 8 and 9, an equation is given. **a.** Find the x- and y-intercepts. **b.** Use the intercepts to graph the line.

8. $4x + 2y = 12$ **9.** $10x - 4y = 20$

  a. _____   **a.** _____

  b.   **b.**

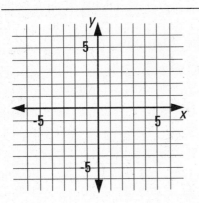
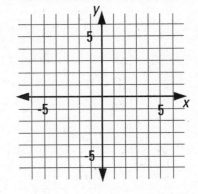

LESSON MASTER

7-9
A

Representations Objective I

In 1 and 2, write an inequality that describes the graph.

1.
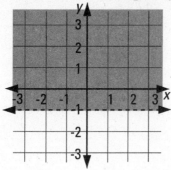

2.
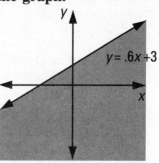

$y = .6x + 3$

_____   _____

In 3 and 4, tell if a. the shading should be above or below the boundary line, and b. the boundary line should be solid or dashed.

3. $y \leq 9x + 3$ a. _____   b. _____

4. $y > x - 6$ a. _____   b. _____

In 5 and 6, graph on the number line and the grid.

5. $x > 4$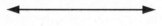

6. $y \leq 8$ ⟵—————————⟶

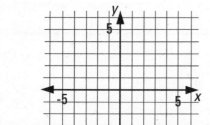

In 7 and 8, graph all points that satisfy the inequality.

7. $y > 3x - 4$

8. $x - 2y > 6$

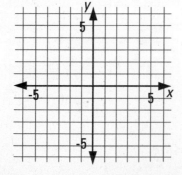

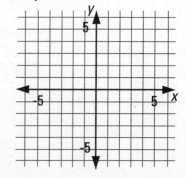

LESSON MASTER

8-1 A

Vocabulary

In 1 and 2, an expression is given. **a.** Write the expression using exponents. **b.** Identify the *base(s)*. **c.** Identify the *exponent(s)*. **d.** Identify the *coefficient*.

1. $25 \cdot x \cdot x \cdot x$

a. _____   b. _____

c. _____   d. _____

2. $6 \cdot a \cdot a \cdot a \cdot a \cdot a \cdot b \cdot b \cdot b$

a. _____   b. _____

c. _____   d. _____

Skills Objective A

In 3–5, evaluate. Give answers to the nearest ten-thousandth.

3. 4^3

4. 1.35^5

5. $40(1 + .06)^{10}$

_____   _____   _____

Uses Objective F

6. Suppose $2500 is invested at 5.6% annual yield for 15 years.

   a. Write an expression for the total amount at the end of this time. _____

   b. Write a calculator key sequence for your expression. _____

7. A bank uses this spreadsheet to show the amount in a savings account earning 7% interest. The principal invested is $600. What formula could be entered in cell

   a. B6? _____

   b. C6? _____

   c. Complete line 6.

   d. What trend do you notice in the annual-interest column?

	A	B	C
			ANNUAL
1	YEAR	BALANCE	INTEREST
2	0	600.00	
3	1	642.00	42.00
4	2	686.94	44.94
5	3	735.03	48.09
6	4		

8. Most credit-cards plans charge interest if the monthly bill is not paid. Suppose an $850 bill is not paid for 3 years. If the annual interest rate is 16%, how much is owed? _____

LESSON MASTER 8-2 A

Skills Objective A

In 1–7, evaluate the expression.

1. 5^0

2. $8^0 \cdot 8^2$

3. $5^6 \cdot 5^0$

_____   _____   _____

4. $(a + 15)^0$ when $a = 6$

5. $\left(\frac{3}{8}\right)^2 + \left(\frac{7}{8}\right)^0$

_____   _____

6. $3 \cdot 10^2 + 4 \cdot 10^1 + 9 \cdot 10^0$

7. $400 \cdot 3^n$ when $n = 0$

_____   _____

Properties Objective E

8. Describe a situation that can be modeled with the expression $100 \cdot 2^0$.

_____

_____

9. A colony of bacteria doubles every 6 hours. How many times will it double in

a. 24 hours?   **b.** 5 days?   **c.** 2 weeks?

_____   _____   _____

Uses Objective G

10. An orange grower introduced a new type of ladybug to his orchards to control pests. He began with 500 ladybugs and feels that the number will naturally increase 5% each month. Based on this information, answer the following questions: In Parts **b** and **c**, round values down to the preceding integer.

a. By how much is the number of ladybugs multiplied each month? _____

b. How many ladybugs will there be after 6 months? _____

c. How many ladybugs will there be after 2 years? _____

▶ **LESSON MASTER 8-2 A** *page 2*

11. Anya has started a new job paying $8 per hour. Assuming that her work is excellent, she will get a 5% raise every 4 months.

   a. After 3 years, how many raises
   will she have gotten?   _____

   b. What will her pay rate be after
   3 years?   _____

   c. If her employer continues to give her
   raises in this way, what will her pay rate be
   after she has been working for 10 years?   _____

12. Jeff wanted to enlarge a drawing on a copy machine. He first enlarged the original by 30%. He then took the copy he just made and fed it through the copy machine, enlarging it by 30%. He did this 3 more times, each time taking the previous copy and enlarging it by 30%. If the original drawing had been 2 inches by 3 inches, did the final copy fit on a sheet of paper $8\frac{1}{2}$ inches by 11 inches? Explain your answer.

_____

_____

_____

Representations Objective I

13. The president of Acme Industries predicts that the sales of a new product will grow by 35% every year for the next 5 years. This year sales were $40,000.

   a. Make a table of values
   showing the sales 0, 1,
   2, 3, 4, and 5 years
   from now.

YEARS	SALES

   b. Graph the sales for the
   first six years.

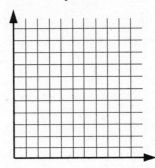

LESSON MASTER

8-3
A

Uses Objective G
Representations Objective I

1. A biologist is studying the effect of a new medicine on the production of antibodies. The antibodies may grow either at a constant rate or exponentially. The biologist studies two cases beginning with 100 antibodies. Case 1: There are 30 more each day. Case 2: There are 20% more each day. Let x = the number of days the antibodies have been growing.

Day	Increase By 30	Increase By 20%
1	130	120
2		
3		
4		
5		
6		
7		
8		
9		
10		

a. Write an expression for Case 1. _____

b. Write an expression for Case 2. _____

c. Complete the table at the right. Round values down to the preceding integer.

d. Which case yields more antibodies after 4 days? _____

e. Which case yields more antibodies after 10 days? _____

f. How many antibodies will there be after 100 days in each case?

Case 1 _____

Case 2 _____

g. Graph the information in the table on the grid at the right.

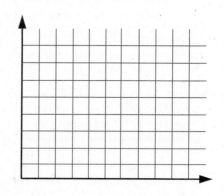

In 2–5, tell which is being described:
(a) *constant increase* or
(b) *exponential growth.*

2.

Mosquitos

Years _____

3. Each day the water level rose $\frac{1}{2}$ inch. _____

4. $2000 + 30x$ _____

5. $450 \cdot 1.8^x$ _____

Name _____

LESSON MASTER **8-4 A**

Questions on SPUR Objectives
See pages 543-545 for objectives.

Uses Objective G

1. Investors in the Get-Rich-Quick Investment company lose about 15% of the value of their money each year.

   a. Fill in the table to show the value of a $2,000 investment for each of the first seven years.

   b. How much was lost the first year?

   _____

   c. How much was lost from the fifth to the sixth year?

   _____

   d. Write an expression for the value of the investment in year x.

   _____

   e. Use trial and error to find the first year in which the value is less than $100. _____

YEAR	VALUE
0	$2,000
1	
2	
3	
4	
5	
6	

2. Amalgamated Industries receives hundreds of applications for each job opening it has. Their selection process is to review the applications and discard 50% of them. Then this is repeated until only one applicant is left. Let n = the number of times that half the applications are discarded.

   a. Write an expression of the form $b \cdot g^n$ to describe the number of people left after the applications have been reviewed n times. _____

   b. If 512 people apply for a job, how many are left when $n = 4$? _____

   c. If 512 people apply, what is the value of n when one person is left? _____

3. In 1993, the national debt was estimated at 4.4 trillion dollars. Suppose this were cut 10% each year. Let x be the number of years since 1993.

   a. Write an equation to describe this situation. _____

   b. What would the deficit be after 20 years? _____

In 4–7, *multiple choice*. Tell if the situation described is:

    (a) exponential growth.   **(b)** exponential decay.

    (c) constant increase.   **(d)** constant decrease.

4. Every year there are 5% fewer patients with the disease. _____

5. With better techniques, farmers are able to increase their
    output 3% each year. _____

6. Each year there are 30 fewer students in the school. _____

7. Every time Joan took the test her score went up 4 points. _____

Representations Objective I

In 8–11, *multiple choice*. Match the graph to the equation.

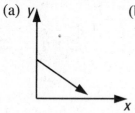 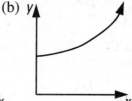 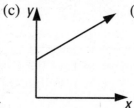 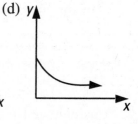

8. $y = 2x + 5$ _____   **9.** $y = -2x + 5$ _____

10. $y = 5 \cdot 1.02^x$ _____   **11.** $y = 5 \cdot .98^x$ _____

12. At Betty's Bargain Shop, the original price of a designer
    dress was $200. The price was marked down 30% for each
    week the dress is not sold. Let x = number of weeks the
    dress is not sold and y = price of the dress.

    a. Write an equation relating x
        and y.

        _____

    b. On the grid at the right,
        graph the price of the dress
        from zero to 10 weeks.

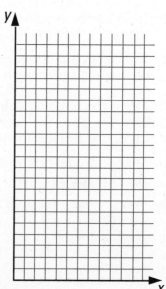

LESSON MASTER

Uses Objective B

In 1–12, simplify the expression.

1. $n^2 \cdot n^6$ _____

2. $y^8 \cdot y$ _____

3. $(x^6)^2$ _____

4. $(5^2)^3$ _____

5. $(k^0)^2$ _____

6. $x^2 \cdot x^4 \cdot x$ _____

7. $a^2 \cdot x^3 \cdot a^7$ _____

8. $n(n^5)^4$ _____

9. $6^2 \cdot 6^2$ _____

10. $2x^3 \cdot 8x^4$ _____

11. $(n \cdot n^4)^3$ _____

12. $x^2(x + x^6)$ _____

Properties Objective E

13. Show how to simplify $(n^2)^4$

   a. by treating n^2 as a chunk.

   _____

   b. by using the Power of a Power Property.

   _____

14. Show how to simplify $a^5 \cdot a$

   a. by using repeated multiplication.

   _____

   b. by using the Product of Powers Property.

   _____

15. Write a multiplication expression that
    uses the Product of Powers Property
    and the value of which is x^{10}.   _____

16. Write an expression that uses the Power
    of a Power Property and the
    value of which is y^{24}.   _____

Name _____

LESSON MASTER **8-6 A**

Questions on SPUR Objectives
See pages 543-545 for objectives.

Skills Objective A

In 1–6, evaluate. Give the answer as a simple fraction.

1. 4^{-1} _____   2. 7^{-2} _____   3. $\left(\frac{1}{3}\right)^{-1}$ _____

4. 11^{-3} _____   5. $5 \cdot 3^{-2}$ _____   6. $19^4 \cdot 19^{-4}$ _____

Skills Objective B

In 7–10, simplify the expression.

7. $a^{-5} \cdot a^6$ _____   8. $n^{-10} \cdot n^3$ _____

9. $a^3 n^{-6} \cdot a^{-3} n^4$ _____   10. $x \cdot x^{-5}$ _____

11. Give examples of three different pairs of
    values of a and b such that $x^a \cdot x^b = x^2$. _____ _____ _____

Properties Objective E

12. How is a^{-n} related to a^n?

_____

13. Simplify $n^{-5} \cdot n^5$ by first applying
    a. the Negative Exponent Property. _____
    b. the Product of Powers Property. _____

Uses Objective G

14. A scientist is studying insects whose population
    doubles every 5 days. There are 4800 insects
    today. How many were there 30 days ago? _____

15. Adria has $4,700 in a bank account that earns 6% interest.

    a. How much did she have in the account 5 years ago? _____

    b. How much will she have 5 years from now? _____

Uses Objective H

16. A test has 15 multiple-choice questions, each with 5 options.
    Write the probability, using a negative exponent, of guessing

    a. all correct answers. _____   b. all wrong answers. _____

Name _____

LESSON MASTER **8-7 A**

Questions on SPUR Objectives
See pages 543-545 for objectives.

Skills Objective A

In 1–3, evaluate the fraction.

1. $\dfrac{2^6}{2^2}$ _____

2. $\dfrac{3^5}{3^7}$ _____

3. $\dfrac{6.8 \cdot 10^5}{1.7 \cdot 10^9}$ _____

Skills Objective B

4. Simplify $\dfrac{n^3}{n^{13}}$. Give your answer

   a. as a fraction. _____   b. using a negative exponent. _____

In 5–11, simplify. Write answers without negative exponents.

5. $\dfrac{a^{10}}{a^7}$ _____

6. $\dfrac{x^2}{x^{14}}$ _____

7. $\dfrac{6x}{3x^5}$ _____

8. $\dfrac{a^3b^5}{a^4b^4}$ _____

9. $\dfrac{12n^3x^{10}}{20n^6x^2}$ _____

10. $\dfrac{(a-6)^8}{(a-6)^9}$ _____

11. $\dfrac{20a^2}{2x} \cdot \dfrac{15x^2}{a^{10}}$ _____

Properties Objective E

12. Write an algebraic fraction that will simplify to $10n^3$ by using the Quotient of Powers Property. _____

13. Explain how to use the Quotient of Powers Property to find the value of x in $\dfrac{4^x}{4^6} = 4^9$.

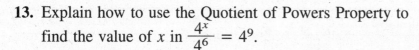

_____

Uses Objective H

14. The North Star is about 680 light-years from Earth. A light-year is $5.879 \cdot 10^{12}$ miles. How many miles away from Earth is the North Star? Give your answer in scientific notation. _____

15. In 1992, the U.S. Internal Revenue Service collected $476 billion in individual income taxes. The U.S. population was about $2.5 \cdot 10^8$. What was the average amount of tax paid per person? _____

LESSON MASTER **8-8**
A

Skills Objective A

In 1–3, tell if the number is *positive* or *negative*.

1. -18^2
2. $(-10)^3$
3. $(-42)^4$

_____ _____ _____

In 4–9, evaluate the expression.

4. -7^2
5. $(2 \cdot 10)^3$
6. $\left(\frac{3}{5}\right)^3$

_____ _____ _____

7. $(3^{-2})^2$
8. $(1.4 \cdot 10^8)^5$
9. $(8.95 \cdot 10^6)^3$

_____ _____ _____

Skills Objective C

In 10–15, simplify the expression.

10. $(3x)^4$ _____
11. $(2a^4)^3$ _____

12. $\left(\frac{8}{9}ny^{10}\right)^2$ _____
13. $10x \cdot (-5x^3)^3$ _____

14. $\left(\frac{6n^4}{x}\right)^2$ _____
15. $\left(\frac{1}{3}x\right)^2 \cdot (6^2)^3$ _____

Properties Objective E

16. Simplify $(ab^5)^3$ by rewriting using

   a. repeated multiplication.

   _____

   b. the Power of a Product Property.

   _____

▶ **LESSON MASTER 8-8 A** *page 2*

17. Simplify $\left(\dfrac{10}{n^a}\right)^4$ by rewriting using

   a. repeated multiplication.

_____

   b. the Power of a Quotient Property.

_____

In 18–21, *multiple choice*. Name the property that is illustrated.

(a) Product of Powers   **(b) Quotient of Powers**

(c) Power of a Power   **(d) Power of a Product**

(e) Power of a Quotient

18. $(x^3)^5 = x^{15}$ _____   **19.** $(3x)^5 = 243x^5$ _____

20. $\left(\dfrac{n}{a^3}\right)^4 = \dfrac{n^4}{a^{12}}$ _____   **21.** $\dfrac{n^4}{n^3} = n$ _____

Uses Objective H

22. The length of one edge of each cube is given. Find the volume of each cube.

   a. x in. _____

   b. $4x$ in. _____

   c. $6x$ in. _____

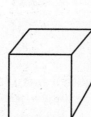
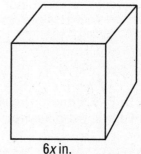

x in.   4*x* in.   6*x* in.

LESSON MASTER **8-9**
A

Uses Objective A

In 1–3, simplify, giving the answer as a simple fraction.

1. $\left(\frac{9}{13}\right)^{-1}$ _____

2. $\left(\frac{7}{8}\right)^{-2}$ _____

3. $\left(\frac{5}{3}\right)^{-3}$ _____

4. *Multiple choice.* Which of the following equals $(4x^{-5})^{-3}$?

(a) $64x^{15}$ (b) $\frac{64}{x^{15}}$ (c) $\frac{x^{15}}{64}$ (d) $\frac{1}{64x^{15}}$

Explain your reasoning.

_____

_____

_____

5. Find a counterexample for the pattern $x^2 \cdot x^4 = x^8$.

_____

_____

Properties Objective D

6. Alicia can't remember how to simplify $\frac{x^6}{x^2}$ but she thinks the
answer is x^3. For each value of x, tell if $\frac{x^6}{x^2} = x^3$ is *true* or *false*.

a. $x = 1$ _____   b. $x = 2$ _____

c. $x = 0$ _____   d. $x = -1$ _____

In 7–9, choose the simplified form of the given expression.
Check your answer by testing a special case.

7. $2x^3 \cdot 8x^{10}$ (a) $16x^{30}$ (b) $16x^{13}$ (c) $10x^{30}$ (d) $10x^{13}$ _____

_____

8. $(5x^2)^3$ (a) $5x^5$ (b) $5x^6$ (c) $125x^5$ (d) $125x^6$ _____

_____

9. $\frac{x^{10}}{x^2}$ (a) x^8 (b) x^5 (c) $\frac{1}{x^8}$ (d) $\frac{1}{x^5}$ _____

_____

LESSON MASTER

9-1
A

Questions on SPUR Objectives
See pages 610-613 for objectives.

Vocabulary

**In 1–6, use the graphs of
parabolas A and B at the right.**

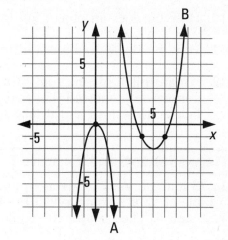

1. What seems to be the vertex of

   a. parabola A?

   _____

   b. parabola B?

   _____

2. What is the axis of symmetry
   of parabola A?

   _____

3. The axis of symmetry of parabola B is the line with equation $x =$ _____.

4. Which parabola opens   **a.** up?   _____

                            b. down?   _____

5. Which parabola has a   **a.** maximum?   _____

                            b. minimum?   _____

6. Give the coordinates of the point that is the reflection image
   of the given point over the parabola's axis of symmetry.

   a. (-2, -8) on parabola A   _____

   b. (3, 2) on parabola B   _____

Skills Objective A

**In 7–9, find both values of x. If answers are
not integers, round to the nearest hundredth.**

7. $24.5 = .5x^2$ **8.** $\frac{3}{5}x^2 = 21$ **9.** $.02x^2 = 6.28$

_____   _____   _____

▶ **LESSON MASTER 9-1 A** *page 2*

In 10–12, use $d = 16t^2$, Galileo's formula relating the
time t in seconds an object falls a distance d in feet.

10. How far does an object fall in 10 seconds? _____

11. How far does an object fall in $2t$ seconds? _____

12. A nail rolled off the roof of a building under
construction and fell 324 feet to the ground
below. How long did it take the nail to fall? _____

Representations Objective F:

In 13 and 14, use the given equation. Make
a table of values using x-values -4, -2, -1, 0,
1, 2, and 4. Then graph the equation.

13. $y = -\frac{1}{4}x^2$

x	y

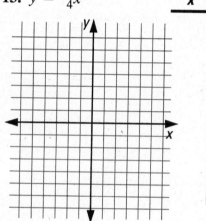

14. $y = 3x^2$

x	y

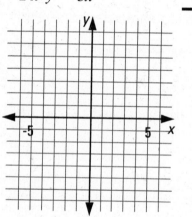

15. From the equation of a parabola, explain how to tell if
its graph opens up or down. Give an example of each
type of equation.

_____

_____

_____

_____

16. Does the parabola with equation $y = -5x^2$ have a
minimum point? Why or why not?

_____

_____

LESSON MASTER 9-2 A

Questions on SPUR Objectives
See pages 610-613 for objectives.

Representations Objective F

In 1 and 2, give an example of an equation of the form
$y = ax^2 + bx + c$ whose graph is a parabola that opens

1. up. _____   2. down _____

In 3 and 4, the graph of a parabola is shown.
a. Give the coordinates of the vertex.
b. Give the y-intercept.
c. Give an equation for the axis of symmetry.

3.

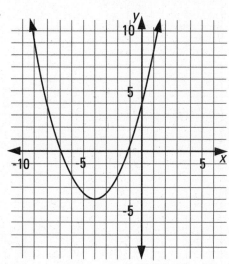

4.

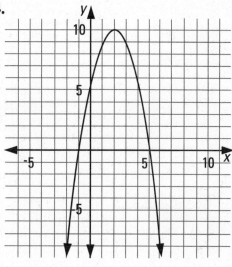

a. _____   a. _____

b. _____   b. _____

c. _____   c. _____

5. a. Complete this table of values for a parabola.

x	-2	-1	0	1	2	3	4	5	6
y	23	14	7	2	-1	-2	-1		

b. What are the coordinates of its vertex? _____

c. What is the y-intercept? _____

d. Does this parabola have a maximum value? _____

e. Does this parabola open up? _____

▶ **LESSON MASTER 9-2 A** *page 2*

In 6 and 7, an equation is given. **a.** Complete the table of
values. **b.** Graph the equation. **c.** Give the coordinates of
the vertex. **d.** Give the *y*-intercept. **e.** Write an equation
for the axis of symmetry.

6. $y = x^2 + 4x + 3$

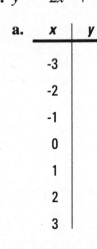

a.

x	y
-3	
-2	
-1	
0	
1	
2	
3	

b.

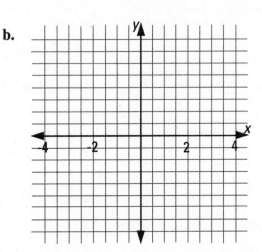

c. _____

d. _____

e. _____

7. $y = -2x^2 + 4x$

a.

x	y
-3	
-2	
-1	
0	
1	
2	
3	

b.

c. _____

d. _____

e. _____

8. a. Use symmetry to complete
the graph on the right.

b. Give its *y*-intercept.

_____

c. Give its *x*-intercepts.

_____

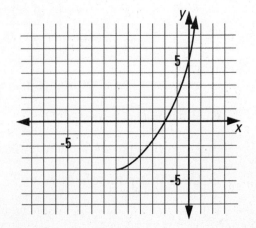

LESSON MASTER

9-3 A

Representations Objective F

1.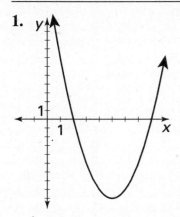

The equation $y = x^2 - 10x + 16$ is graphed at the left.

a. Give the x-coordinate of the vertex. _____

b. Find the y-coordinate of the vertex. _____

c. Write an equation for the axis of symmetry. _____

2. a. On the default window of an automatic grapher, graph these four parabolas.

$y = x^2$ $y = x^2 - 2x$ $y = x^2 - 4x$ $y = x^2 - 6x$

b. Describe how the graphs are similar and how they are different.

_____

_____

_____

c. Describe the graph of $y = x^2 - 50x$.

_____

_____

_____

3. The graph of a parabola is $y = -x^2 + 6x + 60$.
Identify a different window that shows the vertex,
the y-intercept, and both x-intercepts.

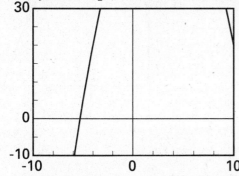

_____

_____

4. Use an automatic grapher to graph $y = x^2 + 4x$ and
$y = -x$ on the same grid. Estimate the coordinates
of the points where the graphs intersect. _____

LESSON MASTER **9-4**
A

Uses Objective E

In 1–5, use the graph at the right.
It illustrates the path of a
football as it leaves the hands of
the quarterback and is thrown to
a receiver. The graph shows the
height *h* after the ball has
traveled *x* yards forward.

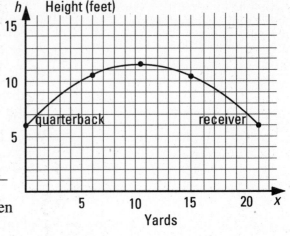

Height (feet)

1. How far is the receiver from
   the quarterback?

   _____

2. About how high is the ball when
   it has moved 2 yards forward?

   _____

3. Is the ball ever 15 feet above the ground?   _____

4. At what distance(s) from the quarterback
   is the ball 10.5 feet above the ground?   _____

5. Most professional basketball players can reach
   10 feet when they jump. Could such a person
   catch the ball if he were positioned 3 feet in
   front of the receiver?   _____

In 6–10, use the graph. It shows the height *h* in feet of
water *t* seconds after leaving the mouth of a fountain.
The equation is $h = -6t^2 + 12t + 10$.

6. What is the greatest
   height the water reaches?   _____

7. How long is the
   water in the air?   _____

8. How high is the
   fountain's mouth?   _____

9. What is the height of the
   water after 2 seconds?   _____

10. Find the height of the
    water after 1.7 seconds.   _____

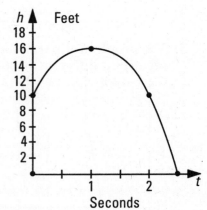

LESSON MASTER **9-5 A**

Questions on SPUR Objectives
See pages 210-213 for objectives.

Skills Objective A

1. Write the Quadratic Formula. _____

In 2–5, find the two values of the expression.

2. $\dfrac{-1 \pm 5}{2}$ _____

3. $\dfrac{15 \pm 3}{12}$ _____

4. $\dfrac{0 \pm \sqrt{49}}{2}$ _____

5. $\dfrac{-6 \pm \sqrt{36 - -220}}{2}$ _____

6. Write the equation $6x + 2x^2 = 4x^2 + 5x + 1$
in standard form. _____

**In 7–10, an equation is given in standard form
a. Give the values of a, b, and c. b. Give the
solutions rounded to the nearest hundredth.**

7. $x^2 - 7x + 6 = 0$ a. _____   b. _____

8. $3y^2 - 10y - 8 = 0$ a. _____   b. _____

9. $v^2 - 11v = 0$ a. _____   b. _____

10. $m^2 + 7m + 2 = 0$ a. _____   b. _____

**In 11–13, a. rewrite the equation in standard form, and
b. give the solution rounded to the nearest hundredth.**

11. $b^2 + 4b = 5$ a. _____   b. _____

12. $5(h^2 - 5h + 2) - 2h = 0$ a. _____   b. _____

13. $m^2 = 1 - 3m$ a. _____   b. _____

14. Show that 0.5 and -3 are solutions of $4x^2 + 10x - 6 = 0$.

_____

_____

Uses Objective E

**In 15–17, use the equation $h = 60t - 16t^2 + 2$, where h is
the height in feet after t seconds of a batted baseball.
Round answers to the nearest tenth.**

15. At what two times is the ball 20 feet in the air? _____

16. When is the ball at 58 feet? _____

17. How long does it take for the ball to hit the ground? _____

LESSON MASTER 9-6 A

Properties Objective D

How many real solutions does a quadratic equation have

1. when the discriminant is negative?   _____

2. when the discriminant is positive?   _____

3. when the discriminant is zero?   _____

In 4–9, use the given equation. a. Find the value of the discriminant. b. Give the number of real solutions.
c. Give all the real solutions to the nearest hundredth.

4. $x^2 + 3x + 1 = 0$

a. _____   b. _____   c. _____

5. $n^2 + n + 8 = 0$

a. _____   b. _____   c. _____

6. $2a^2 + 13a + 6 = 0$

a. _____   b. _____   c. _____

7. $y^2 = 5(y + 2)$

a. _____   b. _____   c. _____

8. $3x^2 + 5x + 7 = 0$

a. _____   b. _____   c. _____

9. $y^2 + 14y + 6 = 9y + 5$

a. _____   b. _____   c. _____

10. For what value of h does $x^2 + 10x + h = 0$
have exactly one solution?   _____

LESSON MASTER 9-7 A

Skills Objective B

1. Use the triangles at the right.

   a. Calculate AB. _____

   b. Express AC as $2 \cdot AB$. _____

   c. Find PQ. _____

   d. Use decimal approximations to verify that
   your answers to Parts **b** and **c** are equal. _____

2. Which of the expressions below equal $\sqrt{72}$? _____

   (a) $2\sqrt{18}$ (b) $3\sqrt{8}$ (c) $4\sqrt{6}$ (d) $6\sqrt{2}$

3. a. State the Product of Square Roots Property.

   _____

   _____

   b. Give an instance of this property. _____

In 4–6, give the exact value of x in simplified form.

4.

5.

6.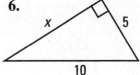

_____   _____   _____

7.

   a. Use the Pythagorean Theorem to
   write an expression for the length
   of the hypotenuse of the triangle. _____

   b. Simplify your answer to Part **a**. _____

In 8–10, simplify. Do not use a calculator.

8. $\sqrt{75} \cdot \sqrt{3}$ _____

9. $\sqrt{9 \cdot 16}$ _____

10. $\sqrt{12^2 \cdot 10^2}$ _____

In 11 and 12, give the exact solution in simplified form.

11. $(3n)^2 = 360$ _____

12. $\dfrac{x}{2} = \dfrac{10}{x}$ _____

13. Simplify.

   a. $\sqrt{50}$ _____

   b. $\sqrt{18}$ _____

   c. $\sqrt{50} + \sqrt{18}$ _____

LESSON MASTER **9-8 A**

Skills Objective C

In 1–6, evaluate the expression.

1. $|-26|$ _____

2. $|4|$ _____

3. ABS $(10 - 5)$ _____

4. $|-6 + 6|$ _____

5. $\sqrt{(-5)^2}$ _____

6. $|-6| + |6|$ _____

7. Fill in the blank. For all, y, $\sqrt{y^2} =$ _____.

In 8–10, solve and check.

8. $|n| = 35$

9. $|x - 6| = 10$

10. $|m + 12| = 4$

Representations Objective G

11. One version of a car-engine cylinder has a diameter of 3.75 in. and must be made with a tolerance of $\pm\,.001$ in. This means that the diameter of the cylinders produced must not be more or less than $3.75 \pm .001$ in.

    a. What is the least diameter acceptable? _____

    b. What is the greatest diameter acceptable? _____

    c. Should a cylinder with a diameter 3.747 by considered defective? _____

    d. Graph all acceptable diameters on this number line.

    e. If d is the diameter of an acceptable cylinder, write an inequality relating $|d - 3.75|$ and $.001$. _____

In 12–13, find the distance between the given points.

12.  _____
    -50   -32

13. _____
    -2   -x

In 14 and 15, give the coordinates of the two points on the number line that are

14. 15 units from the point with coordinate 4. _____ _____

15. 20 units from the point with coordinate -32. _____ _____

LESSON MASTER

9-9
A

Questions on SPUR Objectives
See pages 610-613 for objectives.

Representations Objective G

In 1 and 2, each square represents a city block. Find
the number of blocks it takes to travel from X to Y
a. if you travel on the streets and must go by way
of Z, or b. if you travel "as the crow flies."

1.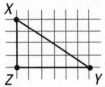

a. _____

b. _____

2.

a. _____

b. _____

In 3–6, use the diagram at the right.
Find each length.

3. AB _____

4. CD _____

5. EF _____

6. GH _____

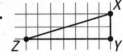

$A = (14, 12)$

$C = (-12, 4)$ $D = (6, 4)$

$B = (14, 2)$

$G = (-12,-1)$ $E = (5, 0)$

$F = (5, -11)$

$H = (-12, -15)$

7. In the diagram, $P = (3, -1)$. Points
A, B, C, and D are each 5 units
from P on the horizontal or vertical
line through P. Give the coordinates
of each point.

A   _____

B   _____

C   _____

D   _____

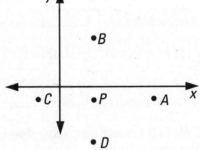

8. Find the coordinates of P shown in the
diagram at the right.

_____

$(-6, 8)$

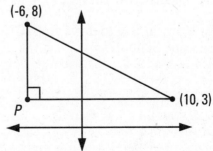

$(10, 3)$

P

9. **a.** Find the coordinates of Q.

    _____

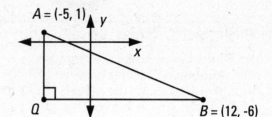

   b. Find AQ. _____

   c. Find BQ. _____

   d. Use the Pythagorean Theorem
   to find AB. _____

10. Write a formula for the distance
    between (a, b) and (j, k). _____

**In 11–14, use the distance formula to find the
distance between the two points. Round answers
to the nearest hundredth.**

11. $(9, 3), (15, 11)$ _____   12. $(-10, 12), (14, 2)$ _____

13. $(12, -14), (15, -7)$ _____   14. $(-10, 1), (-7, 4)$ _____

**In 15–19, use the map at the right. It
shows streets and the locations of
three buildings in a town. The
streets are 1 block apart.**

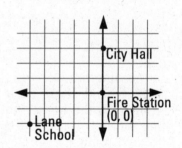

15. What are the coordinates of

    a. City Hall? _____

    b. Lane School? _____

16. How far is it from City Hall to Fire Station? _____

17. How far is it from Lane School to Fire
    Station "as the crow flies"? _____

18. How far is it from Lane School to City Hall
    "as the crow flies"? _____

19. How far is it to drive from City Hall to
    Lane School? _____

LESSON MASTER

10-1
A

Properties Objective E

1. After being simplified, which two of these
   expressions are binomials? _____

   (a) $x + 3x$ (b) $2(y^2 + 9)$ (c) $n + 3$ (d) $5a^2$

2. Give the degree of   **a.** $6x^4$. _____   **b.** x^2y^5. _____

3. Give an example of a monomial of degree 6 in which

   a. the only variable is x. _____

   b. there are two variables, x and y. _____

4. **a.** What is the degree of the monomial 12? _____

   b. Give an example of another monomial
   with the same degree as 12. _____

In 5–7, give the degree of the polynomial.

5. $x^5 - 2x^7$ _____   6. $5n^2 + 7mn - 3$ _____

7. $2x^4 + 5x^4 - 3x^6$ _____

8. Give an example of a trinomial of degree 5. _____

Properties Objective F

In 9 and 10, write as a polynomial in base 10.

9. 7,007,007   10. 2,358

_____   _____

11. Simplify $3 \cdot 10^5 + 4 \cdot 10^3 + 2 \cdot 10^2 + 3 \cdot 10^1$. _____

Representations Objective I

12. Express the area of the figure
    as a polynomial.

13. Make a drawing to represent
    $2x + 6$. Use a rectangular
    arrangement of algebra tiles.

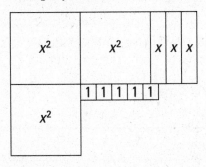

_____

LESSON MASTER 10-2 A

Skills Objective A

In 1–4, simplify the expression.

1. $(8x^2 + 5x - 4) + (6x^2 + 2x - 3)$ _____

2. $(5a^2 - 6a + 1) - (2a^2 - 3a - 2)$ _____

3. $(3n^2 - 5n) - (n^2 + 2n - 8)$ _____

4. $(m^2 + 3m - 12) + (m^2 - 8m + 3)$ _____

Uses Objective G

5. James Garcia won the lottery and will receive $25,000 on June 1st each year for four years. He is planning to invest the money.

   a. Suppose James saves all the prize money, investing it in an account that earns interest at a scale factor x. Complete the table to show how much James will have on June 1 of each year. (Remember that the payments continue for only 4 years, although the money continues to earn interest.)

YEAR	AMOUNT
1	25,000
2	25,000x + 25,000
3	
4	
5	
6	

   b. Calculate how much James would have the sixth year if his interest rate were 5%. _____

   c. How much he would have the sixth year if he could find an investment earning 12%? _____

   d. Suppose the yearly prize had been $250,000 instead of $25,000. Explain how to use the Distributive Property and your answer to Part **c** to easily find out how much he would have the sixth year earning 12% if he saved all his prize money.

   _____

   _____

   _____

In 8–10, use this information: Amy and Anton have just graduated and are each saving money for a down payment on a house. They will each deposit their savings into a special account earning 5.5% interest compounded annually. Their plans are described below.

Amy: Wait and deposit $5,000 at the beginning of the 6th, 7th, and 8th years.

Anton: Deposit $4,000 at the beginning of the 1st, 2nd, and 3rd years.

8. Complete the spreadsheet below.

	A	B	C	D	E
1	Year	Amy's Deposit	Amy's End of Year Balance	Anton's Deposit	Anton's End of Year Balance
2	1	0		4,000	
3	2	0		4,000	8,672.10
4	3	0		4,000	
5	4	0		0	
6	5	0		0	
7	6	5,000		0	
8	7	5,000		0	
9	8	5,000		0	

9. What formula could be used to calculate the value in

   a. cell C9? _____

   _____

   b. cell E9? _____

   _____

10. Who has more money at the end of 8 years? How much more?

   _____

LESSON MASTER

Skills Objective C

In 1–10, simplify the expression.

1. $3(x + 5)$

2. $2y(3y^2 + 10y - 6)$

3. $4x(2x)$

4. $4x(2 + x)$

5. $-4ab(a^2 - 6ab + 9)$

6. $2m^4(m^5 - 3)$

7. $8(x + 9) + x$

8. $3(x^2 + 4x) + x(x - 15)$

9. $n(2n + 9) - 6(n - 1)$

10. $x(2a + 1) + 6a(-x + 9)$

In 11–14, fill in the blank.

11. $2(x + \underline{\hspace{1cm}}) = 2x + 18$

12. $6n(\underline{\hspace{1cm}} + 9) = 24n^2 + 54n$

13. $x^2(x^2 + \underline{\hspace{1cm}}) = x^4 + x^2y$

14. $\underline{\hspace{1cm}} (2y + 7) = -6y - 21$

Representations Objective I

In 15–16, a rectangle is shown. a. Express the area as length • width. b. Express the area as the sum of smaller areas. c. Write an equation using the expressions from parts a and b for the area of the rectangle.

15.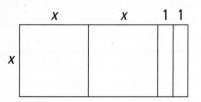

a. _____

b. _____

c. _____

16.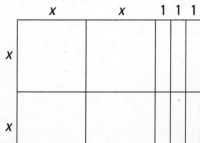

a. _____

b. _____

c. _____

LESSON MASTER

Skills Objective B

In 1–5, multiply and simplify.

1. $(n + 3)(n^2 + 5n + 9)$

_____

2. $(y - 2)(5y^2 + y - 4)$

_____

3. $(x^2 + 2x + 3)(4x^2 - 8x + 1)$

_____

4. $(5m + x - 1)(m - 6x - 8)$

_____

5. $(x + 8)(x + 3)(x - 2)$ _____

Representations Objective I

6. **a.** Express the area of the large rectangle as length · width.

_____

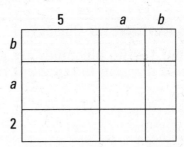

b. Express this area as the sum of nine smaller areas.

_____

_____

7. A cube has edges 5 cm long. A larger cube had edges a cm longer.

a. What is the volume of the first cube? _____

b. What is the volume of the larger cube? _____

c. How much greater is the volume of the larger cube than the volume of the smaller one? _____

8. **a.** Write an expression for the volume of the box at the right.

_____

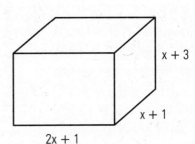

b. Check your answer to Part **a** by substituting 6 for x.

_____

_____

LESSON MASTER **10-5 A**

Skills Objective C

In 1–7, multiply and simplify.

1. $(n + 8)(n + 2)$ **2.** $(x - 6)(x + 8)$ **3.** $(y - 3)(y - 9)$

_____   _____   _____

4. $(4a + 5)(4a - 5)$ **5.** $(a - b)(a + 5b)$ **6.** $(n^2 + 2n)(n + 5)$

_____   _____   _____

7. $(3 + \sqrt{5})(10 - \sqrt{5})$ _____

In 8 and 9, fill in the blanks.

8. $(n + 2)(n - \underline{\quad}) = n^2 - 5n - 14$ **9.** $(x + \underline{\quad})(x + 6) = x^2 + 7x + 6$

Representations Objective I

**In 10 and 11, two binomials are given. a. Simplify the product.
b. Draw a diagram to represent the multiplication.**

10. $(x + 5)(x + 4)$ **11.** $(2x + 3)(2x + 1)$

     a. _____   **a.** _____

     b.   **b.**

12. A fountain is in the shape of a rectangle 20 ft long and 8 ft wide. A sidewalk x feet wide surrounds the fountain.

     a. What is the length of the outer rectangle? _____

     b. What is the width of the outer rectangle? _____

     c. Write an expression for the combined area of the fountain and the sidewalk. _____

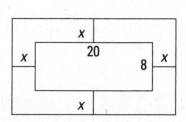

LESSON MASTER **10-6 A**

Skills Objective C

In 1–9, multiply and simplify.

1. $(x + 7)(x + 4)$ **2.** $(3m - 5)(m + 3)$ **3.** $(d - 3)(2d - 7)$

_____   _____   _____

4. $(2a + 6)(3a - 9)$ **5.** $(x - y)(2x + 2y)$ **6.** $(n + 3a)(n - 4a)$

_____   _____   _____

7. $(n - 6)(n + 6)$ **8.** $(5a + 2b)(5a - 2b)$ **9.** $(4 + \sqrt{3})(4 - \sqrt{3})$

_____   _____   _____

10. a. Write the Difference of Two Squares Pattern.

_____

     b. Give an instance of the Difference of Two Squares Pattern.

_____

11. Why is $x^2 + 9$ *not* a difference of two squares?

_____

12. Why is $y^2 - 11$ *not* a difference of two squares?

_____

13. Explain how you could use the Difference of Two Squares
Pattern to calculate $101 \cdot 99$ mentally.

_____

Skills Objective D

14. According to the Perfect Square Pattern, $(n + k)^2 = $ _____.

15. According to the Perfect Square Pattern, $(m - y)^2 = $ _____.

▶ **LESSON MASTER 10-6 A** *page 2*

16. Expand $(n + 5)^2$ by

    a. rewriting the expression as a multiplication of $n + 5$ by itself and using the FOIL algorithm.

_____

    b. using the Perfect Square Pattern.

_____

In 17–20, expand and simplify.

17. $(4x + 1)^2$ **18.** $(2n - 9)^2$

_____   _____

19. $(8 + \sqrt{2})^2$ **20.** $(n - w)^2 + (n + w)^2$

_____   _____

Representations Objective I

21. a. Express the area of the figure at the right as the square of a binomial.

    _____

    b. Express the area as the sum of smaller areas.

    _____

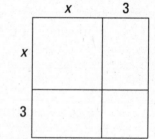

For 22 and 23, an expression is given. a. Draw a figure whose area is given by the expression. b. Write the polynomial represented by your drawing in Part a.

22. $(x + 4)^2$ **23.** $(3x + 2)^2$

    a.   **a.**

    b. _____   **b.** _____

LESSON MASTER **10-7 A**

Uses Objective H

In 1 and 2, use the following information and the chi-square critical-value table given below.

A psychologist wanted to see whether people associated particular colors with musical selections. He performed an experiment in which he played a musical selection and then asked each listener which one of the following four colors they associated with that selection. His results are listed in the table.

Colors	Percent of Listeners Choosing Color
Red	19%
Blue	21%
Green	24%
Yellow	36%

1. Suppose the psychologist had questioned 80 people.

   a. Find the number of people choosing each color.

   Red _____   Blue _____

   Green _____   Yellow _____

   b. The psychologist believes that there is no tendency for people to associate any particular color with the music. How many people would then be expected to choose each color?

   Red _____   Blue _____

   Green _____   Yellow _____

   c. Use the actual numbers and the psychologist's expected numbers to calculate the chi-square statistic for this experiment.   _____

▶ **LESSON MASTER 10-7 A** *page 2*

Critical Chi-Square Values

n − 1	.10	.05	.01	.001
1	2.71	3.84	6.63	10.8
2	4.61	5.99	9.21	13.8
3	6.25	7.81	11.34	16.3
4	7.78	9.49	13.28	18.5
5	9.24	11.07	15.09	20.5
6	10.6	12.6	16.8	22.5
7	12.0	14.1	18.5	24.3
8	13.4	15.5	20.1	26.1
9	14.7	16.9	21.7	27.9
10	16.0	18.3	23.2	29.6

d. Refer to the Critical Chi-Square Values table above. Using your answer to Part **c**, what can you conclude about the psychologist's belief?

_____

_____

_____

_____

2. Suppose the psychologist had asked 200 people. Answer the same questions that you did for Question 1 for 200 people.

a. Red _____ Blue _____

    Green _____ Yellow _____

b. Red _____ Blue _____

    Green _____ Yellow _____

c. _____

d. _____

_____

_____

3. From Questions 1 and 2, what can you say about the relationship between sample size and the conclusions reached in the experiment?

_____

_____

_____

LESSON MASTER 11-1 A

Representations Objective H

1. a. Use a brace ({) to write the
system of equations shown on
this graph.

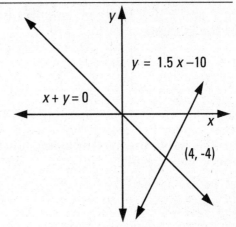

$y = 1.5\,x - 10$

$x + y = 0$

$(4, -4)$

b. What is the solution to the system?

_____

c. Write a check to show that your
answer to Part **b** is a solution to
the system from Part **a**.

_____

_____

In 2 and 3, a system is given. **a.** Graph the two lines.
b. Give the solution. **c.** If there is a solution, check it.

2. $\begin{cases} y = x + 1 \\ y = -2x + 4 \end{cases}$

3. $\begin{cases} y = -3x + 4 \\ 6x + 2y = 2 \end{cases}$

a.

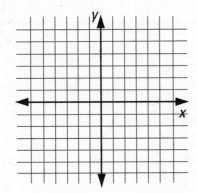

a.

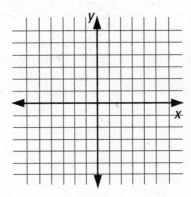

b. _____

b. _____

c. _____

c. _____

_____

_____

LESSON MASTER 11-2 A

Skills Objective A

In 1 and 2, tell if the given point is the solution
of the system.

1. $(6, 9)$ $\begin{cases} y = 4x - 15 \\ y = \frac{1}{2}x - 3 \end{cases}$

_____

2. $x = 15, y = 11$ $\begin{cases} y = \frac{2}{3}x + 1 \\ y = x - 4 \end{cases}$

_____

In 3–6, solve the system using substitution and
check your results.

3. $\begin{cases} y = -4x + 32 \\ y = x - 3 \end{cases}$

4. $\begin{cases} h = \quad v + 5 \\ h = \quad -\frac{1}{2}v + 2 \end{cases}$

5. $\begin{cases} d = r + 1 \\ d = -2r - 2 \end{cases}$

6. $\begin{cases} y = \frac{1}{2}x - 2 \\ y = \frac{3}{2}x - 7 \end{cases}$

Uses Objective F

7. A river is flooded and the height of the water is
rising. The levee along the river is 30 feet high
and workers are building it higher at the rate of
$\frac{1}{2}$ ft per hour. The water height is 28 feet and it
is rising $\frac{3}{4}$ ft each hour.

a. Describe this situation with a system
of equations.

_____

b. Solve the system to find when the
water will reach the top of the levee
if these rates continue.

_____

c. If, in fact, the water stops rising after
12 hours, will it rise above the levee
and cause a flood?

_____

LESSON MASTER 11-3 A

Questions on SPUR Objectives
See pages 715–717 for objectives.

Skills Objective A

In 1–6, solve the system by substitution. Check the solution.

1. $\begin{cases} y = x + 4 \\ 2x + y = 1 \end{cases}$

2. $\begin{cases} y = 2x \\ 7x + 5y = 34 \end{cases}$

3. $\begin{cases} x = y - 3 \\ 4x + 2y = 6 \end{cases}$

4. $\begin{cases} y = 2x - 8 \\ x - y = 3 \end{cases}$

5. $\begin{cases} x + y = 15 \\ x - y = 7 \end{cases}$

6. $\begin{cases} x - y = 3 \\ 2x - 3y = -1 \end{cases}$

Uses Objective F

7. A theater sells children's tickets for $4 and adult tickets for $7. One night 575 tickets worth $3575 were sold. How many adults and how many children bought tickets?

_____

8. Students are chosen for a scholarship based on their scores on tests of mathematics and verbal achievement. A student's qualifying score is found by doubling his verbal score and adding his math score. Gretchen's math score was 54 points higher than her verbal score. Her qualifying score was 1782. Find Gretchen's math and verbal scores.

_____

9. Huey, Dewey, and Louie want model rockets so each one is saving his allowance. Huey says, "I have 5 more dollars than you do, Louie." Dewey says, "I have twice as much as you do, Louie." Louie says, "Together we have $31.00. That's enough to buy a rocket." How much does each have?

_____

LESSON MASTER 11-4 A

Questions on SPUR Objectives
See pages 715-717 for objectives.

Skills Objective B

In 1 and 2, write the equation that results when the left sides and the right sides of the two equations are added.

1. $\begin{cases} 4x + 3y = 8 \\ x - 3y = 22 \end{cases}$ _____

2. $\begin{cases} -5x + 3y = 16 \\ 5x - 10y = 12 \end{cases}$ _____

In 3–8, solve the system. Check your solution.

3. $\begin{cases} x + y = 30 \\ x - y = 6 \end{cases}$

4. $\begin{cases} -10a + 7b = 25 \\ 10a + 5b = 35 \end{cases}$

5. $\begin{cases} 2x + y = 4 \\ x - y = 2 \end{cases}$

6. $\begin{cases} 4n + 3m = 11 \\ 4n + 5m = 5 \end{cases}$

7. $\begin{cases} 3t + 2u = 7 \\ -2t + 2u = -2 \end{cases}$

8. $\begin{cases} -2x - 3y = 4 \\ 2x - 4y = 3 \end{cases}$

Uses Objective F

9. At a concession stand, two pretzels and two boxes of popcorn cost $3.50. Two pretzels and four boxes of popcorn cost $6.00. Find the cost of each item. _____

10. Beth and Carol had dinner at a cafe. The total bill was $14.40. Beth's meal cost $2.00 more than Carol's. Find the cost of each person's meal. _____

11. When Rosa flew from Boston to Cleveland, the plane was going against the wind and traveled only 120 mph. However, on the return trip, the plane traveled with the wind at 230 mph. What was the plane's speed without wind? What was the average speed of the wind? _____

LESSON MASTER

11-5
A

Skills Objective C

1. Solve the system $\begin{cases} x - 2y = 1 \\ 4x + y = 22 \end{cases}$

   a. by multiplying and adding to eliminate y. _____

   b. by multiplying and adding to eliminate x. _____

2. Consider the system $\begin{cases} 5a - 4b = 14 \\ 2a + 3b = 1 \end{cases}$.

   a. Tell what to multiply each equation by to eliminate a. _____

   b. Tell what to multiply each equation by to eliminate b. _____

   c. Solve the system and check your solution. _____

In 3–8, solve the system, and check your solution.

3. $\begin{cases} 2e + 3f = 18 \\ 5e - f = 11 \end{cases}$

4. $\begin{cases} 2x + 6y = -2 \\ 5x - 3y = 31 \end{cases}$

5. $\begin{cases} 10x + 3y = 23 \\ 5x + 12y = 22 \end{cases}$

6. $\begin{cases} 4w + 5z = 7 \\ 6w - 2z = -18 \end{cases}$

7. $\begin{cases} 3m + 2n = 10 \\ 2m + 5n = 3 \end{cases}$

8. $\begin{cases} -8r + 3s = 10 \\ 10r - 2s = -2 \end{cases}$

Uses Objective F

9. A manager of an apartment building needs to buy 45 air conditioners, one for each apartment. She has planned to spend $6,000 on the air conditioners. Two models are available, one at $110 and the other at $160. How many of each should she buy to spend $6,000? _____

10. For Mother's Day a florist sells two bouquets. A bouquet of 5 roses and 10 carnations costs $8.75. A larger bouquet has a dozen roses and 15 carnations. It costs $16.50. Find the cost of one rose and of one carnation. _____

LESSON MASTER 11-6 A

Properties Objective E

1. The line $y = -4x + 5$ is parallel to which two
of the following lines?   _____

    (a) $y = 3x + 5$ (b) $y = -4x + 3$ (c) $4x + y = 3$

2. **a.** Explain how to tell if two lines in a system are parallel.

    _____

    _____

  b. Are the lines in this system parallel? $\begin{cases} 6x - 2y = 8 \\ -15x + 10y = 30 \end{cases}$ _____

3. Consider the system $\begin{cases} y = 3x + 2 \\ 9x - 3y = -6 \end{cases}$.

  a. Find three ordered pairs that are
    solutions to $y = 3x + 2$.   _____

  b. Show that each ordered pair from Part **a** is also a
    solution to $9x - 3y = -6$.

    _____

  c. How many solutions does this system have? _____

**In 4–7, tell if the system has *no solutions*, *one solution*,
or *infinitely many solutions*.**

4. $\begin{cases} 2x - 5y = 7 \\ 4x - 10y = 14 \end{cases}$ _____
    5. $\begin{cases} 4a - b = -13 \\ 2a + 10b = 46 \end{cases}$ _____

6. $\begin{cases} 10x + 6y = 18 \\ 3y = 2 - 5x \end{cases}$ _____
    7. $\begin{cases} 2(x + 3) = y \\ 4x - y = 9 \end{cases}$ _____

Uses Objective F

8. When Gary Liu stands on a scale with his dog Daisy, their
combined weight is 173 lb. When Gary stands on the scale
alone, his weight is 173 lb less Daisy's weight.

  a. Write a system of equations to
    describe this situation.   _____

  b. How many solutions does this
    system have?   _____

► **LESSON MASTER 11-6 A** *page 2*

Representations Objective H

In 9 and 10, a system of equations is given. a. Graph
the system. b. Give the solution.

9. $\begin{cases} y = 3x + 5 \\ y = 3x - 1 \end{cases}$

10. $\begin{cases} 6x + 3y = -12 \\ y = -2x - 4 \end{cases}$

a.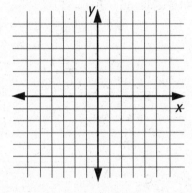

a.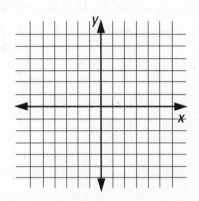

b. _____

b. _____

In 11–13, a. give a system of two equations with the
indicated number of solutions, and b. graph the system.

11. one   **12.** none   **13.** infinitely many

a. _____   a. _____   a. _____

b.   b.   b.

LESSON MASTER 11-7 A

Properties Objective D

1. a. Add $8x$ to both sides of $3 - 8x > 1 - 8x$.
What sentence results? _____

b. Describe the solutions to $3 - 8x > 1 - 8x$. _____

Multiple choice. **In 2–5, tell if the sentence is**

(a) *sometimes true.*   **(b)** *always true.*   **(c)** *never true.*

2. $3y + 6 = 3(y + 2)$ _____   **3.** $n + 6 < n + 2$ _____

4. $x - 9 = 9 - x$ _____   **5.** $12 - 2x < -2(x - 6)$ _____

In 6 and 7, give an example of an inequality that

6. has no solution. _____

7. is true for all real numbers. _____

In 8 and 9, solve.

8. $3 + 15x = 3 + 2x$ **9.** $\frac{1}{3}(12x - 9) < (x + 9) - (6 - 3x)$

Uses Objective F

10. Listed below are the price plans for boxes of computer
disks sold by four mail-order companies.

A: $1.75 per box plus $5.00 shipping fee, labels included
B: $2.00 per box plus $3.00 shipping fee, labels included
C: $2.00 per box plus $5.00 shipping fee, labels included
D: $1.75 per box plus $3.00 shipping fee plus $.25 per box for labels

a. Let x = number of boxes of disks ordered. Write an
expression for the cost of x boxes of disks
(with labels) from each company.

A _____ B _____

C _____ D _____

b. When does A charge more than B? _____

c. When does B charge more than C? _____

d. When are the costs from B and D the same? _____

LESSON MASTER **11-8 A**

Uses Objective G

1. A family plans to spend between $20 and $30 at a carnival. Rides cost $1.50 and games are $1.00. Let x = the number of rides and y = the number of games.

   a. Give two combinations of rides and games that fit within the family's budget.

   _____

   _____

   b. Describe this situation with a system of four inequalities.

   _____

   _____

   _____

   _____

   c. Graph the system at the right.

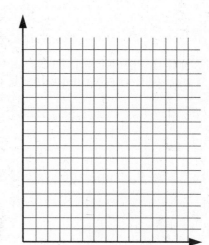

Representations Objective I

2. *Multiple choice.* Which point is a solution to $\begin{cases} y < 2x + 5 \\ y > -x + 2 \end{cases}$? _____

   (a) (1, 0)   (b) (2, 9)   (c) (4, -1)   (d) (-1, 2)

3. Write a system of inequalities to describe points in quadrant II. _____

4. Describe the graph of $y = 0$, $x < 0$.

   _____

▶ **LESSON MASTER 11-8 A** *page 2*

In 5–7, use the graph at the right. It is
the graph of the following system
of inequalities.

$$\begin{cases} y > 0 \\ y > -x + 3 \\ y < -x + 10 \end{cases}$$

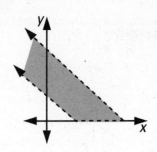

Tell if the given point is a solution of the system.
If not, tell which inequality it fails to satisfy.

5. (5, 8) _____   6. (6, -1) _____

7. (-1, 2) _____

In 8 and 9, graph the system of inequalities.

8. $\begin{cases} x > 0 \\ y > 0 \\ 2x + y < 8 \end{cases}$ 9. $\begin{cases} y < 0 \\ x > 0 \\ y > 3x - 5 \end{cases}$

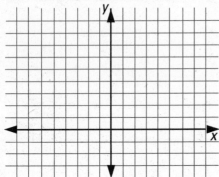   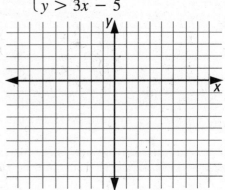

In 10 and 11, write a system of inequalities to describe the graph.

10.

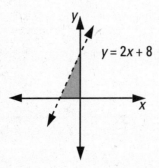

$y = 2x + 8$

11.

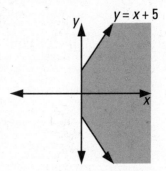

$y = x + 5$

_____   _____

LESSON MASTER

12-1 A

Skills Objective A

1. List all the pairs of integers whose product is 36.

_____

_____

2. List all the pairs of integers whose product is -15.

_____

_____

In 3–6, write the prime factorization.

3. 252 _____ **4.** 504 _____

5. 1155 _____ **6.** 3773 _____

In 7–9, determine whether or not the number is prime.

7. 127 _____ **8.** 1001 _____ **9.** 2079 _____

In 10–13, the product and the sum of a pair of
integers is given. Find the numbers.

10. product: 24, sum: 11 _____ **11.** product: 8, sum: 9 _____

12. product: -14, sum: 5 _____ **13.** product: -42, sum: -1 _____

In 14–16, rewrite the fraction in lowest terms.

14. $\frac{5625}{2835}$ _____ **15.** $\frac{6768}{288}$ _____ **16.** $\frac{3024}{588}$ _____

Properties Objective E

In 17 and 18, give the number of factors in the
prime factorization.

17. 8^3 _____ **18.** 7^4 _____

19. Explain why the number $7^{20} + 7^{21} + 7^{22}$ could *not* be prime.

_____

_____

LESSON MASTER **12-2 A**

Questions on SPUR Objectives
See pages 769-771 for objectives.

Skills Objective B

1. List all the factors of $9x^2$. _____

In 2–5, tell whether or not the polynomial is prime.

2. $2x + 10$ 3. $n + 12$ 4. $y^2 + 15y$ 5. $ab + 3y$

_____   _____   _____   _____

In 6–9, find the greatest common factor of the monomials.

6. $18n$ and 3 _____   7. $2x^4$ and $10x^2$ _____

8. d^3 and d^2 _____   9. $10x^3$, $15x^2$ and $20x^2y^2$ _____

In 10–13, fill in the blanks.

10. $12x + 20 = 4(\underline{\quad} + \underline{\quad})$ 11. $3n^4 - 5n^3 = n^3(\underline{\quad} - \underline{\quad})$

12. $6y^2 - 12y + 21 = 3(\underline{\quad} + \underline{\quad} + \underline{\quad})$

13. $4a^2b + 16a^3b^2 = 4a^2b(\underline{\quad} + \underline{\quad})$

In 14–17, factor the polynomial completely.

14. $15x - 35$ _____   15. $24x^2 - 8x$ _____

16. $20 - 6x + 2$ _____   17. $18a^4 - a^5x$ _____

Representations Objective J

In 18 and 19, make a drawing with algebra tiles showing a rectangle that has the given area.

18. $x^2 + 3x$ 19. $2x + 8$

20. Given the fraction $\dfrac{3x^4 + 2x}{x}$, $(x \neq 0)$,
    a. factor the numerator, and
    b. simplify the fraction.   a.  _____   b. _____

LESSON MASTER 12-3 A

Skills Objective C

In 1–6, factor the expression.

1. $n^2 + 13n + 22$

_____

2. $a^2 - 5a - 14$

_____

3. $-12 + x^2 + 4x$

_____

4. $x^3 - 8x^2 + 15x$

_____

5. $y^2 - 5y$

_____

6. $x^2 - 49$

_____

Properties Objective G

7. Explain why the trinomial $x^2 + 5x + 7$ cannot be factored over the integers.

_____

_____

8. *Multiple choice.* Which polynomial can be factored over the integers? _____

(a) $x^2 - 4x + 7$ (b) $x^2 - x + 6$ (c) $x^2 + 5x - 8$ (d) $x^2 - 3x - 2$

Representations Objective J

Show that each expression can be factored by drawing a rectangle using algebra tiles.

9. $x^2 + 6x + 5$

10. $x^2 + 6x + 9$

LESSON MASTER 12-4 A

Skills Objective D

In 1–6, solve by factoring.

1. $x^2 - 2x - 15 = 0$

2. $0 = x^2 - 10x + 21$

3. $12m = -35 - m^2$

4. $y^2 + 2y - 35 = 0$

5. $h^2 + h - 42 = 0$

6. $g^2 + 5g = 24$

Properties Objective F

In 7–11, tell what equations result from applying the Zero Product Property.

7. $(x + 8)(x - 10) = 0$ _____

8. $n(n - 3) = 0$ _____

9. $x^2 + 11x + 18 = 0$ _____

10. $y^2 + 12y = 0$ _____

11. $(n + 3)(n + 8)(n - 7) = 0$ _____

Uses Objective I

12. A rectangle with area 48 cm^2 is 8 cm longer than it is wide.

    a. Write an expression for the length
    of the rectangle. _____

    b. Write an equation of the form
    length · width = area. _____

    c. Find the rectangle's length and
    width. _____

13. A circular mirror with radius r is surrounded
    by a circular gilt frame 3 cm wide. If the total
    area of the mirror and the frame is 2025π cm^2,
    what is the radius of the mirror? _____

LESSON MASTER 12-5 A

Skills Objective C

In 1–6, factor.

1. $2x^2 + 7x + 5$

2. $6n^2 - 7n + 2$

_____

3. $7x^2 + 3x - 4$

4. $13y + 6 + 5y^2$

_____

5. $4n^2 - 4n - 3$

6. $6a^2 - 11a - 10$

_____

7. Find two possible values of k for which $5x^2 + kx + 11$ can be factored, and show the factorization.

_____

8. **a.** Factor the greatest common factor from $10y^3 + 26y^2 - 12y$. _____

   b. Complete the factorization of $10y^3 + 26y^2 - 12y$ by factoring the trinomial in your answer from Part **a**. _____

Skills Objective D

In 9–11, solve the equation. Factor when necessary.

9. $(3x - 5)(2x + 9) = 0$ 10. $25a^2 + 30a + 9 = 0$ 11. $2n^2 + 5n = 12$

LESSON MASTER

12-6
A

Uses Objective I

In 1 and 2, use this information: **The area of a rectangular field is 9100 square meters and its perimeter is 400 meters.**

1. Use the Babylonian method to find the dimensions of the field. Show your work.

_____

2. Use a modern method to find the dimensions of the field. Show your work.

_____

In 3 and 4, use this information: **A rectangular garden covering 1500 square feet is enclosed by 160 feet of fencing.**

3. Use the Babylonian method to find the dimensions of the garden. Show your work.

_____

4. Use a modern method to find the dimensions of the garden. Show your work.

_____

Name _____

LESSON MASTER **12-7**
A

Questions on SPUR Objectives
See pages 769-771 for objectives.

Properties Objective H

In 1–9, tell whether the number is *rational* or *irrational*.

1. $\frac{2}{3}$

2. $\sqrt{2}$

3. $1.\overline{3}$

_____   _____   _____

4. 12

5. π

6. $\sqrt{25}$

_____   _____   _____

7. $\sqrt{5}$

8. 8.1

9. $2.7\overline{3}$

_____   _____   _____

In 10–12, find a simple fraction equal to the number.

10. $21\frac{48}{61}$

11. $5.86\overline{7}$

12. $13.\overline{521}$

_____   _____   _____

13. Determine whether the solutions to the equation
$4x^2 - 1 = 0$ are *rational* or *irrational*. Explain
your reasoning.

_____

_____

_____

14. Can rational numbers be found in real situations?
If so, give an example.

_____

_____

LESSON MASTER 12-8 A

Questions on SPUR Objectives
See pages 769-771 for objectives.

Properties Objective G

1. Suppose f, g, and h are integers. How can you tell whether the polynomial $fx^2 + gx + h$ is factorable over the integers?

_____

In 2–5, tell whether or not the polynomial is prime.

2. $6x^2 + 19x + 10$ _____ 3. $5y^2 + 10y + 4$ _____

4. $3u^2 + 13u + 14$ _____ 5. $25v + 3 + 2v^2$ _____

In 6–9, a polynomial is given. a. Calculate the discriminant of the polynomial. b. Use the discriminant to determine whether the expression can be factored over the integers.

6. $16a^2 - 18a + 9$ a. _____   b. _____

7. $m^2 + 15m - 17$ a. _____   b. _____

8. $4z^2 + 15z + 5$ a. _____   b. _____

9. $10c^2 - 29c + 10$ a. _____   b. _____

10. Find two integer factors of 15 whose sum is 8. What does this tell you about $x^2 + 8x + 15$?

_____

11. Consider the polynomial $ax^2 + 7x - 15$. For what value(s) of a from 1 to 7 is the polynomial factorable? _____

12. The equation $y = 3x^2 + 7x - 4$ is graphed at the right. Are the x-intercepts rational? Explain your thinking.

_____

_____

_____

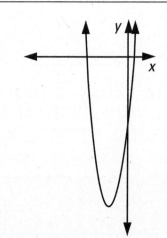

LESSON MASTER  13-1 A

Properties Objective C

In 1–4, explain why the equation, inequality, or set of points *does* or *does not* represent a function.

1. $y = |x|$

_____

2. $y < x + 3$

_____

3. $6x - 2y = 5$

_____

4. $\{(-3, 1), (0, 12), (2, -4), (5, 12)\}$

_____

5. Give a set of ordered pairs that is *not* a function.

_____

Representations Objectives H and I

6.

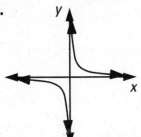

The graph of $y = \dfrac{1}{x}$ is shown at the left. Is this the graph of a function? Explain why or why not.

_____

_____

_____

In 7 and 8, **a.** graph the equation and **b.** tell if it describes a function.

7. $x = 3$

a.

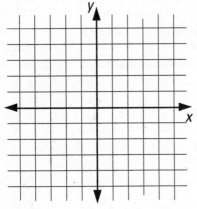

8. $x - y = 5$

a.

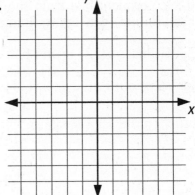

b. _____   **b.** _____

LESSON MASTER 13-2 A

Vocabulary

In 1 and 2, tell how the expression or equation should be read.

1. $f(x) = x + 9$ _____

2. ABS(5) _____

Skills Objective A

In 3–6, evaluate the expression.

3. SQR(144) _____

4. $f(10)$ if $f(x) = 4x + 12$ _____

5. $f\left(\frac{7}{10}\right)$ if $f(x) = 5x$ _____

6. $g(-6)$ if $g(x) = x^2 + x + 1$ _____

7. Let $f(x) = -2x + 8$. Find

a. $f(4)$. _____   b. $f(1)$. _____   c. $\dfrac{f(4) - f(1)}{4 - 1}$. _____

8. Suppose $f(x) = 9x - 15$. For what value of x is $f(x) = -12$? _____

Uses Objective E

9. A laboratory technician tested the growth of bacteria. When the experiment had been running for t hours the number of bacteria $n(t)$ was approximated by $n(t) = 250 \cdot (1.12)^t$.

a. Evaluate $n(12) - n(11)$. _____

b. What does $n(12) - n(11)$ represent?

_____

_____

10. Let $K(y)$ = Kurt's height in year y and $B(y)$ = Brad's height in year y.

    a. What does it mean about the boys if $K(y) < B(y)$?

_____

_____

    b. What does it mean if $K(y) = B(y)$?

_____

_____

    c. What does it mean if $K(1990) < K(1991)$?

_____

_____

Representations Objective I

In 11 and 12, the equation of a function is given.
a. Graph the function. b. Give the *y*-intercept.

11. $f(x) = 4x - 8$ **12.** $f(x) = x^2 - 5$

    a.   **a.**

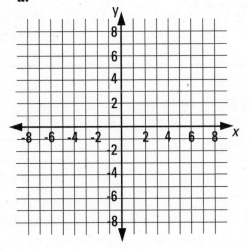 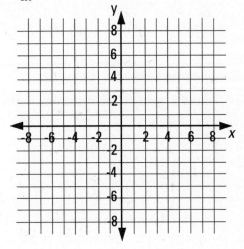

    b. _____   **b.** _____

LESSON MASTER **13-3 A**

Skills Objective A

1. If $f(x) = 2|3x + 2|$, find $f(-2)$. _____

2. If $g(x) = -|5x|$, find $g(-1)$. _____

In 3 and 4, solve.

3. $|x + 2| = 3$

4. $|3m - 2| + 1 = 5$

_____   _____

Uses Objective E

5. *Multiple choice.* The actual inside diameter of certain
   sewer tiles is slightly more or less than 0.8 meter. Let
   $f(d) = $ the error in a tile with inside diameter d. Which
   equation relates $f(d)$ and d? _____

   (a) $f(d) = |d|$ (b) $f(d) = |0.8 - d|$ (c) $f(d) = -|d + 0.8|$

6. *Multiple choice.* An incubator was programmed so that
   its temperature inside starts to rise at 84°F and then
   rise for 4 hours at a constant rate of 2°F per hour until
   reaching a maximum temperature of 92°F. The
   temperature then falls at the same rate. Which equation
   gives the temperature $f(t)$ in terms of time t? _____

   (a) $f(t) = |t|$ (b) $f(t) = |92 - t|$ (c) $f(t) = -2|t - 4| + 92$

Representations Objective I

In 7 and 8, graph the function with the given equation.

7. $f(x) = |2x|$

8. $y = -|x - 2| + 2$

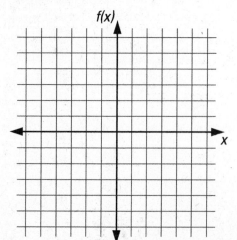

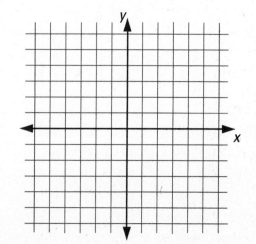

LESSON MASTER 13-4 A

Properties Objective D

1. **a.** Give the domain of f when $f(x) = \dfrac{4}{x + 6}$. _____

   b. Give the domain of g when $g(x) = \dfrac{x + 9}{x - 5}$. _____

   c. Give an example of a function whose domain is the set of all real numbers except 8. _____

In 2–6, a function is described. Give its domain and its range.

2. $\{(-6, 5), (-3, 1), (0, 2), (2, 10)\}$ _____ _____

3. 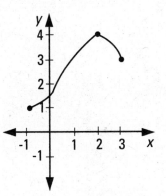   4.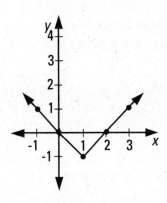

_____   _____

_____   _____

5. $g(x) = \sqrt{x} + 8$ _____   _____

6. $s(x) = \dfrac{|x|}{x}$ _____   _____

Uses Objective E

7. The table at the right shows a system used to describe the intensity of a hurricane.

   a. Give three possible (category, wind speed) ordered pairs.

   _____

   b. Give three possible (wind speed, category) ordered pairs.

   _____

   c. Is either set of all ordered pairs in Parts **a** and **b** a function? Explain why or why not.

   _____

Category	Wind Speed
1 (weak)	74–95 mph
2 (moderate)	96–110 mph
3 (strong)	111–130 mph
4 (very strong)	131–155 mph
5 (devastating)	156+ mph

LESSON MASTER **13-5** **A**

Questions on SPUR Objectives
See pages 821-823 for objectives.

Uses Objective F

1. Gregor Mendel was the first scientist to connect probability to genetics. He crossed snapdragons that have red flowers with snapdragons that have white flowers. He obtained three kinds of offspring: snapdragons with red flowers, snapdragons with white flowers, and snapdragons with pink flowers. He found $P(\text{red}) = \frac{1}{4}$ and $P(\text{white}) = \frac{1}{4}$ where $P(\text{color})$ means the probability that the offspring of snapdragons will have flowers of color x.

   a. What is $P(\text{pink})$? _____

   b. What is the range of this function? _____

2. Two dice are tossed. Find $P(\text{sum is even})$ and $P(\text{sum is odd})$. Explain your method.

   _____

   _____

   _____

   _____

3. Suppose for families with 2 children, if $P(n) =$ the probability that n children in the family can roll their tongue, then $P(1) = \frac{1}{8}$ and $P(2) = \frac{1}{64}$.

   a. What does $P(0)$ represent?

   _____

   _____

   b. Find $P(0)$. _____

Representations Objective I

4. The fair spinner at the right is divided into six congruent parts. The point value of each region is labeled. Let $P(n)$ = probability of getting n points on a spin.

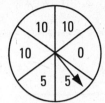

   a. Find $P(0)$, $P(5)$, and $P(10)$.

_____

_____

   b. Graph $P(n)$.

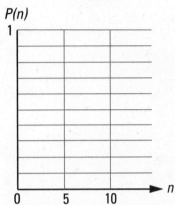

5. A cookie jar contains 15 oatmeal cookies, 6 chocolate-chip cookies, and 9 peanut-butter cookies. You reach in and choose a cookie at random.

   a. Find P(choosing an oatmeal cookie).

_____

   b. Graph the probability it will be oatmeal (OM), chocolate chip (CC), or peanut butter (PB).

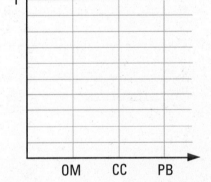

6. There are three stoplights on Meg's way to work. Let $P(n)$ = the probability that Meg will have to stop at exactly n red lights.

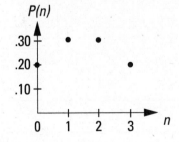

   a. What is the probability that Meg will not have to stop at all three lights?

_____

   b. What is $P(0) + P(1) + P(2) + P(3)$?

_____

LESSON MASTER 13-6 A

Questions on SPUR Objectives
See pages 821-823 for objectives.

Representations Objective J

In 1 and 2, an equation is given. a. Complete the table of x- and y-values. b. Plot the ordered pairs and connect them with a smooth curve. c. Describe the graph.

1. $y = x^4 - x^3 + 2x^2 - 2x + 4$

a.

x	y
-3	
-2	
-1	
0	
1	
2	
3	

b.

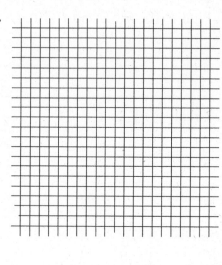

c. _____

_____

2. $y = x^3 + 2x^2 - 4x - 5$

a.

x	y
-3	
-2	
-1	
0	
1	
2	
3	

b.

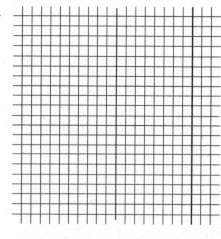

c. _____

_____

_____

Name _____

In 3–6, use an automatic grapher. A function is given.
a. Find a window which shows all the *x*- and *y*-intercepts
of the functon. b. Draw the graph of this function as it
appears on your automatic grapher.

3. $f(x) = x^3 + 3x^2 + 3x + 2$

a. _____

_____

b.

4. $g(x) = x^4 - 2x^2 + 1$

a. _____

_____

b.

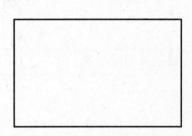

5. $h(x) = 2x^5 - 3x^4 - 4x^3 + 1$

a. _____

_____

b.

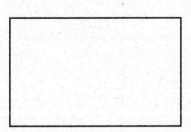

6. $y = x^3 - 2x + 1$

a. _____

_____

b.

LESSON MASTER **13-7**
A

Skills Objective B

1. Write a calculator key sequence to find tan 48°.

_____

In 2 and 3, round to the nearest hundredth.

2. tan 15°   **3.** tan 71.5°

_____   _____

Uses Objective G

4.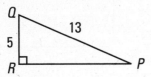

a. Find the length of segment *RP*.

_____

b. Find the tangent of angle *P*.

_____

In 5 and 6, find the slope of the line.

5.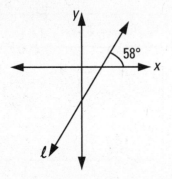

6.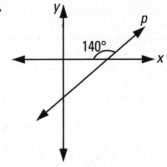

_____   _____

7. What is the tangent of the acute angle formed by the
line $5x - 2y = 3$ and the positive ray of the *x*-axis? _____

8.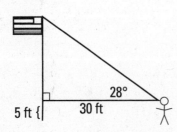

When Roberto stands 30 feet away from
the flagpole, he has to look up 29° to see
the top. His eyes are 5 ft above the
ground. How high is the flagpole?

_____

LESSON MASTER 13-8 A

Questions on SPUR Objectives
See pages 821-823 for objectives.

Skills Objective B

In 1–6, give a decimal approximation rounded
to the nearest hundredth.

1. cos 12° _____

2. sin 78° _____

3. the reciprocal of 6.02 _____

4. log(0.125) _____

5. 12! _____

6. log(1000) _____

In 7–10, give an example of a real number that is *not*
in the domain of the function and whose values are found
by pressing the indicated calculator key. If all real
numbers are in the domain of the function, write "all."

7. $\boxed{x^2}$

8. $\boxed{!}$

9. $\boxed{1/x}$

10. $\boxed{\sqrt{}}$

_____ _____ _____ _____

11. There is a function related to the common logarithm called the
natural logarithm, or $y = \ln x$. The natural logarithm of a
number x is the power to which the special number $e \approx 2.718$
must be raised to equal the number x. Experiment with your
calculator to find the domain of this function. The key on your
calculator for the natural logarithm function is labeled $\boxed{\ln}$.

_____

In 12 and 13, use an automatic grapher to graph
the function. a. Determine the domain of the function.
b. Determine the range of the function. c. Give the
values of x, if any, that will produce an error message
on your grapher.

12. $y = \sin x$

a. _____

b. _____

c. _____

13. $y = \log x$

a. _____

b. _____

c. _____

LESSON MASTER 1-1 A

Vocabulary

1. What is an *equation*? **a sentence containing verb "="**

2. What does the symbol "≤" mean? **is less than or equal to**

3. Write an inequality that compares $\frac{4}{7}$ and $\frac{1}{2}$ and that
   a. uses the symbol "<." $\dfrac{1}{2} < \dfrac{4}{7}$
   b. uses the symbol ">." $\dfrac{4}{7} > \dfrac{1}{2}$

4. Which of the symbols =, ≠, ≈, >, ≥, <, and ≤
   make a true statement when written in the blank?
   $\dfrac{2}{3}$ __?__ .66   **≠, ≈, >, ≥**

5. Let p = the population of the United States.
   a. Write an inequality for this statement:
      The population of the United
      States is greater than 250 million. **$p > 250$ million**
   b. Give a number that is a solution
      to the sentence in Part a. **Sample: 250,000,001**

6. Give an example of an open sentence.
   Samples: $3 = \frac{x}{2}$, $m = \frac{a}{b}$, $x + y = 5$

7. Let B = Bill's batting average. Write a sentence in words that
   fits the algebraic sentence $B > .275$.
   Bill's batting average is greater than .275.

Skills Objective A

8. Which of the numbers 2, 4, and 6
   are solutions to $n + 5 = 2 \cdot n - 1$?
   6

9. Which of the numbers 2, 3, and 4
   are solutions to $4 \cdot k + 8 > 16$?
   3, 4

10. Give three solutions to the open sentence $m < 6.5$.
    Samples are given.
    $m = -5$ $m = 4.8$ $m = 6.4$

11. Find both solutions to $x^2 = 81$. **$x = 9$ $x = -9$**

12. Give an example of an inequality
    for which 10 is a solution. **Samples: $x < 11$, $x \geq 9$**

LESSON MASTER 1-2 A

Properties Objective E

1. Give an example of a number that is an integer. **-7, 0, 85**

2. Give an example of a number that is not an integer. **$-\frac{7}{8}$, π, 0.93**

3. Give an example of a number that is
   an integer but is not a whole number. **-10, -4, -1**

4. Is the interval that is the graph of $5 \leq n \leq 18.5$
   open, closed, or *neither* open nor closed? **closed**

Samples are given for 1–3.

Uses Objective I

Multiple choice. In 5–6, choose the most reasonable domain
for the variable.

   (a) set of integers   (b) set of real numbers
   (c) set of positive integers (d) set of positive real numbers

5. y = the year a battle was fought by the Roman army **a**

6. s = the number of hot dogs sold at a baseball park **c**

Representations Objective L

In 7–8, graph the solution set on a number line.

7. $n < 2$, when n is an integer

8. $1.2 \leq y < 1.8$ when y is a
   real number

Multiple choice. In 9–12, tell which domain was used in the
graph of $y < 2$.

   (a) set of integers   (b) set of real numbers
   (c) set of positive integers (d) set of positive real numbers

9. **b**

10. **d**

11. **a**

12. **c**

LESSON MASTER 1-3 A

Skills Objective B

1. For the Venn diagram at the left,
   list the elements of **{-2, 0, 1,**
   a. $J \cup K$. **3, 5, 6, 9, 15}**
   b. $J \cap K$. **{6, 9}**

2. Let R = {5, 10, 15, 20} and T = {11, 12, 13, 14, 15}.
   a. Give the union of R and T. **{5, 10, 11, 12, 13, 15, 20}**
   b. Give the intersection of R and T. **{15}**

3. Let A = the set of divisors of 12 and B = the
   set of divisors of 30. List the elements of $A \cap B$. **{1, 2, 3, 6}**

Properties Objective E

Samples are given for 4 and 5.

4. Give an example of two sets of E and F for which $E \cap F = \emptyset$.
   $E = $ **{-3, -1, 2, 4}** $F = $ **{-2, 0, 1, 3, 5}**

5. Let $P \cap Q = \{1, 2\}$, $P \cup Q = \{1, 2, 3, 4\}$.
   Draw a Venn diagram to show sets of P
   and Q that fit this description. There
   are several possible diagrams.

Representations Objective L

6. Graph the solution sets. For a domain, use the set of real numbers.
   a. $n > 10$
   b. $n \leq 24$
   c. $n > 10$ and $n \leq 24$
   d. $n < 10$ or $n \geq 24$

7. In 1993, an unmarried U.S. taxpayer paid 28% income tax
   on earnings described by the inequality $\$22,101 < x \leq \$53,500$.
   a. Graph this interval.
   b. Describe the interval with two inequalities linked by the word "and."
   **$x > 22,101$ and $x \leq 53,500$ or $22,101 < x$
   and $53,500 \geq x$**

LESSON MASTER 1-4 A

Vocabulary

1. Give an example of a numerical expression. **$7 \cdot 3^2 + 5 - 9$**

2. Give an example of an algebraic expression. **$5x^2 + y + 3$**

3. What does it mean to "evaluate an expression"?
   to find the numerical value of the expression

Skills Objective C

4. Evaluate $12y + 3$ when
   a. $y = 4$. **51**   b. $y = 2.5$. **33**   c. $y = 0$. **3**

For 5–10, if the expression is algebraic write "algebraic." If the
expression is numerical, evaluate it.

5. $\dfrac{3 + 15}{2(3)}$ **3**   6. $4(2 + 7) - k$ **algebraic**

7. $40 - 3(11)$ **7**   8. $2(3 + 2)^2 + 9$ **59**

9. $a - \dfrac{4}{n}$ **algebraic**   10. $3^5 - 5^3$ **118**

11. The perimeter of this pentagon is
    $3a + 2b$. Find the perimeter when
    $a = 15.4$ and $b = 6.5$.
    59.2

12. What is the value of the BASIC expression
    $(2 * 8 + 5)/(30 - 23)$? **3**

13. Write a key sequence
    to enter the following
    expression into a calculator. $\dfrac{40 \cdot 2 + 8}{4^2}$
    **(40 ⊗ 2 ⊕ 8)
    ⊕ 4 y^x =**

14. a. Evaluate $10y^3$ when $y = 2$. **80**
    b. Evaluate $(10y)^3$ when $y = 2$. **8,000**
    c. Find a value for y so that the value of
       $10y^3$ is the same as the value for $(10y)^3$. **$y = 0$**

Lesson Master 1-5 A

LESSON MASTER **1-5 A**

Vocabulary

1. **a.** *Multiple choice.* Which of the equations below is a formula for *y* in terms of other variables?

   (a) $Ax + By = C$ (b) $x = \dfrac{C - By}{A}$ (c) $y = \dfrac{C - Ax}{B}$

   c

   b. What are the other variables?   **A, B, C, x**

Uses Objective J

2. A concession stand sells sandwiches and cold drinks. The price *P* of an order, including sales tax, is given by the formula

   $$P = 1.05(3S + 75D)$$

   where *S* = the number of sandwiches ordered and *D* = the number of drinks ordered. Find the cost of each order, rounded up to the next cent.

   a. 4 sandwiches and 5 drinks   **$16.54**

   b. 6 drinks   **$4.73**

3. Use the formula $V = \frac{4}{3}\pi r^3$ for the volume of a sphere. Find the volume of a softball with radius 3.8 in.   **≈ 229.9 in³**

4. Suppose you have *n* dollars and you save 8 dollars each week for *w* weeks. The amount of money *m* you have will be given by

   $$m = n + 8w.$$

   How much money will you have after

   a. 5 weeks if you start with $25?   **$65**

   b. one year if you start with $60?   **$476**

5. The cost *C* for *y* cubic yards of cement is given by

   $$C = 37.50y + 65.$$

   Find the cost of 6.5 cubic yards of cement.   **$308.75**

5

Lesson Master 1-6 A

LESSON MASTER **1-6 A**

Vocabulary

1. What is the name for the symbol "$\sqrt{\ }$"?   **radical sign**

2. Give an example of two numbers that
   a. are perfect squares.   **Samples: 25, 64**
   b. are *not* perfect squares.   **Samples: 2, 17**

Skills Objectives C and D

In 3 and 4, give **a.** the exact square roots of the given number and **b.** the approximate square roots, rounded to the nearest hundredth.

3. 41 **a.** $\sqrt{41}, -\sqrt{41}$ 4. 325 **a.** $\sqrt{325}, -\sqrt{325}$

   b. **6.40, -6.40**   **b.** **18.03, -18.03**

5. The area of a square is 517 sq ft. Give
   a. the exact length of a side of the square.   **$\sqrt{517}$ ft**
   b. the length of a side rounded to the nearest hundredth.   **22.74 ft**

In 6–12, evaluate without a calculator.

6. $\sqrt{49} + \sqrt{1}$ __**8**__   7. $\sqrt{36} + \sqrt{64}$ __**10**__   8. $\sqrt{36 + 64}$ __**14**__

9. $8\sqrt{25}$ __**40**__   10. $11\sqrt{5} \cdot \sqrt{5}$ __**55**__   11. $(\sqrt{12})^2$ __**12**__

12. Evaluate each expression to the nearest thousandth when *s* = 10 and *t* = 50.

   a. $\sqrt{st}$ **22.361**   **b.** $s\sqrt{t}$ **70.711**

13. If an object is dropped and it falls *d* feet in *t* seconds, then $t = \sqrt{\dfrac{d}{16}}$.

   If an object were dropped from the top of the Empire State building, which is 1250 ft tall, how long would it take to hit the ground?   **≈ 8.8 sec**

Properties Objective F

14. What does the Square of the Square Root Property tell you about $\sqrt{y^2} \cdot \sqrt{y^2}$?

   For non-negative y^2, $\sqrt{y^2} \cdot \sqrt{y^2} = y^2$.

6

Lesson Master 1-7 A

LESSON MASTER **1-7 A**

Vocabulary

In 1 and 2, consider the pattern $a\sqrt{4} = \sqrt{a \cdot 4}$. When $a = 1$, this is true, because $1 \cdot \sqrt{4} = \sqrt{1 \cdot 4}$. When $a = 9$, this is false, because $9\sqrt{4} \neq \sqrt{9 \cdot 4}$. Which value of *a*

1. gives an *instance* of $a\sqrt{4} = \sqrt{a \cdot 4}$?   **a = 1**

2. gives a *counterexample* to $a\sqrt{4} = \sqrt{a \cdot 4}$?   **a = 9**

Properties Objective G

In 3–5, give two instances of the pattern.   **Samples are given.**

3. $\dfrac{x^3}{x} = x^2$

   $\dfrac{3^3}{3} = 3^2$ **(9)** $\dfrac{(-5)^3}{-5} = (-5)^2$ **(25)**

4. $5(a + b) = 5a + 5b$

   $5(-4 + 6) = 5 \cdot -4 + 5 \cdot 6$ **(10)**

   $5(99 + 1) = 5 \cdot 99 + 5 \cdot 1$ **(100)**

5. *h* hours and *m* minutes is $60h + m$ minutes.

   3 hr and 5 min is $3 \cdot 60 + 5$ min **(485 min)**

   0 hr and 7 min is $0 \cdot 60 + 7$ min **(7 min)**

In 6 and 7, give a counterexample to show that the pattern is not always true.   **Samples are given.**

6. $n^2 = 2n$ **$(-2)^2 \neq 2(-2)$**   **(4 ≠ -4)**

7. $2a + b = 2b + a$ **$2 \cdot 5 + 3 \neq 2 \cdot 3 + 5$**   **(13 ≠ 11)**

7 ▶

Lesson Master 1-7 A page 2

▶ **LESSON MASTER 1-7 A** *page 2*

Properties Objective H

8.

A piece of string is cut into pieces. Describe the following pattern using one variable.

   1 cut makes $1 + 1$ pieces of string.

   2 cuts make $2 + 1$ pieces of string.

   3 cuts make $3 + 1$ pieces of string.

   c cuts make $c + 1$ pieces of string.

9. **a.** Describe this pattern with one variable.   **Samples are given for b–d.**

   $\frac{1}{6} < 6$

   $\frac{1}{8.5} < 8.5$

   $\frac{1}{57} < 57$ **$\dfrac{1}{x} < x$**

   b. Find another integer that gives an instance of this pattern.   **$10 \left(\frac{1}{10} < 10\right)$**

   c. Find an integer that gives a counterexample to the pattern.   **$-5 \left(\frac{1}{-5} \not< -5\right)$**

   d. Find a non-integer that gives a counterexample to the pattern.   **$0.25 \left(\frac{1}{0.25} \not< 0.25\right)$**

10. Use two variables to describe this pattern.

   $3 + 3 + 8 = 2 \cdot 3 + 8$

   $55 + 55 + 1 = 2 \cdot 55 + 1$

   $.4 + .4 + .6 = 2 \cdot .4 + .6$ **$x + x + y = 2y + y$**

8

LESSON MASTER 1-8 A

Questions on SPUR Objectives
See pages 65-68 for objectives.

Vocabulary

In 1–3, name a. the hypotenuse and b. the legs.

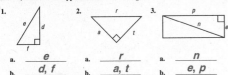

1. a. __e__
   b. __d, f__

2. a. __r__
   b. __a, t__

3. a. __n__
   b. __e, p__

Uses Objective K

4. To drive from town A to town B you can travel 8 miles east and then 4 miles south.
   a. How long is the drive from A to B? **12 mi**
   b. A shortcut path from A directly to B is shown by the dotted line. How long is the shortcut? **≈ 8.94 mi**
   c. How much shorter is the shortcut than the road that goes east and then south? **≈ 3.06 mi**

5. 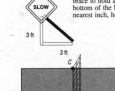 A road construction worker needs to make a diagonal brace to hold a sign. The pole is 3 ft high, and the bottom of the brace will be 3 ft from the pole. To the nearest inch, how long must the brace be? **4 ft 3 in.**

In 6 and 7, use the diagram of a doubles tennis court, which measures 78 ft by 36 ft.

6. To the nearest foot, how far is it from A to B? **86 ft**

7. To the nearest foot, how far is it from A to C? **53 ft**

9

LESSON MASTER 1-9 A

Questions on SPUR Objectives
See pages 65-68 for objectives.

Properties Objective G

1. 5 squares 6 squares 7 squares
   a. Sketch the next two instances in the pattern above. 8 squares 9 squares
   b. Fill in the chart below.

Number of Squares	5	6	7	8	9	...	n
Perimeter	12	14	16	18	20	...	$2n + 2$

2. Triangles and blocks are used to make the pattern below.
   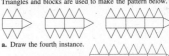
   a. Draw the fourth instance.
   b. How many blocks will be needed to make the hundredth instance? How many will be triangles? Explain how you got your answers.
   501 blocks; 401 triangles; Sample: The number of rectangles is 100, and the number of triangles is 100·4 + 1, or 401; the total is 501.

Properties Objective H

For 3 and 4, use the chart at the right.

a	1	2	3	4
b	7	8	9	10

3. Does the equation $b = 7a$ describe the numbers in the table? Explain why or why not.
   No; sample: the value of $7a$ is 14, not 8.

4. Does the equation $b = a + 6$ describe the numbers in the table? Explain why or why not.
   Yes; sample: For each a value in the table, the b value agrees with the equation.

10 ▶

▶ **LESSON MASTER 1-9 A** *page 2*

5. The diagram below shows a brick wall made from whole and half-bricks.
   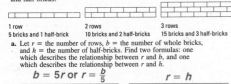
   1 row — 5 bricks and 1 half-brick
   2 rows — 10 bricks and 2 half-bricks
   3 rows — 15 bricks and 3 half-bricks
   a. Let r = the number of rows, b = the number of whole bricks, and h = the number of half-bricks. Find two formulas: one which describes the relationship between r and b, and one which describes the relationship between r and h.
   $b = 5r$ or $r = \frac{b}{5}$ **$r = h$**
   b. If the wall has 12 rows, how many whole and half-bricks will be used?
   60 whole, 12 half-bricks

In 6-8, use the pattern below.

1 square / 2 triangles / perimeter = 6
2 squares / 4 triangles / perimeter = 10
3 squares / 6 triangles / perimeter = 14
4 squares / 8 triangles / perimeter = 18

6. Let s = the number of squares and t = the number of triangles. Describe the relationship between s and t.
   $t = 2s$ or $s = \frac{t}{2}$

7. Explain why the formula $p = 6s$ does not relate the perimeter p of the figure to the number of squares.
   Sample: When $s = 2$, $p = 10 \ne 12$; when $s = 3$, $p = 14 \ne 18$; when $s = 4$, $p = 18 \ne 24$.

8. A correct formula giving the perimeter in terms of the number of squares is $p = 4s + 2$. Show that the formula works for a figure with 6 squares by drawing the figure and finding its perimeter.
    $p = 4 \cdot 6 + 2 = 26$

11

LESSON MASTER 2-1 A

Questions on SPUR Objectives
See pages 136-138 for objectives.

Skills Objective F

In 1–3, tell whether the statement illustrates the Commutative Property of Multiplication or the Associative Property of Multiplication.

1. $3(7x) = 21x$ **Assoc. Prop.**
2. $1.5(2y^3) = 1.5(y^3 \cdot 2)$ **Commut. Prop.**
3. Twenty 10-ounce bars of chocolate contain the same amount of chocolate as ten 20-ounce bars. **Commut. Prop.**

In 4–7, simplify.

4. $50x^2 \cdot 2 \cdot 19$ **$1900x^2$**
5. $8a \cdot 7b$ **$56ab$**
6. $10x \cdot 2xy \cdot 3xz$ **$60x^3yz$**
7. $\frac{2}{5}p \cdot 5q$ **$2pq$**

Uses Objective G

In 8 and 9, find the area of the shaded region.

8. **80 ft²**
9. **51 cm²**

10. A building code requires that the windows in a room have glass area equal to 15% of the floor area. An architect's plan has two 3-ft-by-4-ft windows in a 12-ft-by-15-ft room. Does this plan meet the code? Why or why not?
    No; area of windows is 24 ft²; area of room is 180 ft²; 24 is only 13.3% of 180.

11. How many boxes 1″ × 2″ × 3″ can be packed in a carton 2 ft × 3 ft × 5 ft? **8,640 boxes**

Representations Objective J

12. 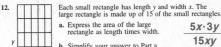 Each small rectangle has length y and width x. The large rectangle is made up of 15 of the small rectangles.
    a. Express the area of the large rectangle as length times width. **$5x \cdot 3y$**
    b. Simplify your answer to Part a. **$15xy$**

12

LESSON MASTER 2-2 A

Properties Objective F

In 1–6, give the reciprocal.

1. $\frac{2}{3}$ $\frac{3}{2}$ 2. $1\frac{2}{5}$ $\frac{5}{7}$ 3. $\frac{-4}{p}$ $-\frac{p}{4}$

4. $\frac{1}{10}$ **10**   5. -0.25   **-4**   6. $\frac{6}{a+b}$ $\frac{a+b}{6}$

7. Write a key sequence you could use to find the reciprocal of 1.333 on a calculator that has no reciprocal key.

Sample: 1 ÷ 1.33 =

8. *Multiple choice.* Which equation means that x and y are reciprocals?   **d**

  (a) $\frac{x}{y} = 1$ (b) $1x = y$ (c) $x + y = 1$

  (d) $xy = 1$ (e) $\frac{x}{y} = \frac{y}{x}$

In 9–12, a. tell whether the two numbers are reciprocals, and b. briefly explain why or why not.

9. 5 and 0.2   a. **yes**   b. **$5 \cdot 0.2 = 1$**

10. $-\frac{1}{3}$ and 3   a. **no**   b. **$-\frac{1}{3} \cdot 3 = -1$**

11. -1 and -1   a. **yes**   b. **$-1 \cdot -1 = 1$**

12. 100,000 and 0.000001   a. **no**   b. **$100{,}000 \cdot 0.000001 = 0.1$**

In 13–16, a. simplify, and b. name the property you used.

13. $10(3x - 3x)$ a. **0**   b. **Multiplication Property of Zero**

14. $(a + b) \cdot \frac{1}{a+b}$ a. **1**   b. **Property of Reciprocals**

15. $\frac{4.7x^2}{4.7x^2} \cdot 5$ a. **5**   b. **Multiplication Identity Property of 1**

16. $(3t + 1)(2t - 2)(t + 3)(0)$ a. **0**   b. **Multiplication Property of Zero**

LESSON MASTER 2-3 A

Skills Objective A

In 1–4, use the Equal Fractions Property to simplify.

1. $\frac{5t}{3tb}$ $\frac{5}{3b}$ 2. $\frac{24a^2}{8}$ $3a^2$ 3. $\frac{5000x}{2000xy}$ $\frac{5}{2y}$ 4. $\frac{85m^3n}{100m^2x}$ $\frac{17mn}{20x}$

In 5–16, multiply. Simplify the product where possible.

5. $\frac{2}{3} \cdot \frac{x}{8}$ $\frac{x}{12}$ 6. $\frac{2x}{3} \cdot \frac{15}{x}$ 10   7. $\frac{15a}{2a} \cdot \frac{1}{5}$ $\frac{3}{2}$

8. $\frac{x^2}{8y} \cdot \frac{9}{4x^2}$ $\frac{9}{32y}$ 9. $6 \cdot \frac{2x}{3}$ $4x$ 10. $\frac{1}{0.85} \cdot 0.85t$ t

11. $\frac{nx}{5} \cdot \frac{11}{ny}$ $\frac{11x}{5y}$ 12. $45 \cdot \frac{7}{15s}$ $\frac{21}{s}$ 13. $\frac{1200a}{11x} \cdot \frac{55x^2}{400a^2}$ $\frac{15x}{a}$

14. $\frac{7200r}{35r^2} \cdot \frac{5}{1200}$ $\frac{6}{7r}$ 15. $\frac{5}{2n} \cdot \frac{3x}{25} \cdot \frac{4n}{9x}$ $\frac{2}{15}$ 16. $\frac{10y}{3} \cdot \frac{30x}{7y} \cdot \frac{42}{500}$ $\frac{6x}{5y}$

17. The largest rectangle at the right has base x and height y.

  a. If all the smallest rectangles have the same dimensions, what is the area of the shaded region? $\frac{2xy}{5}$

  b. What product of algebraic fractions is represented by the product of length and width of the shaded region? $\frac{2x}{4} \cdot \frac{4y}{5}$

18. An architect designed a seminar room to be two fifths as long and one third as wide as an adjoining lecture hall. Compare the areas of the two rooms.

Sample: The area of the room is $\frac{2}{15}$ the area of the hall; the area of the hall is ℓw, and the area of the room is $\frac{2}{5}\ell \cdot \frac{1}{3}w$, or $\frac{2}{15}\ell w$.

LESSON MASTER 2-4 A

Uses Objective H

1. One of the longest trips reported for a single fill-up was about 1690 miles in a Toyota LandCruiser which had a total fuel capacity of 38.2 gallons in two tanks. Compute the mpg (miles per gallon) for this trip.

   ≈44.2 mpg

2. A construction company asserts that it can build one mile of road every 10 days. How many miles can it build in one day?

   $\frac{1}{10}$ mi

3. A ream of paper is 500 sheets. Four reams weight 20 pounds. What is the weight of 5000 sheets of paper?

   50 lb

4. A 250-gram serving of spaghetti with meatballs contains 330 calories in food energy.

  a. What is the number of calories per gram?

   $1.32\frac{\text{cal}}{\text{g}}$

  b. A 150-pound person will burn about 9.5 calories for every minute of jogging. How long will it take to burn off the calories from a 250-gram serving of spaghetti?

   ≈34.7 min

5. The Japanese *Shinkansen* (bullet train) averages about 165 kilometers per hour between Tokyo and Osaka. What is this rate in meters per second?

   $≈45.8\frac{\text{m}}{\text{sec}}$

6. The label on a frozen turkey says ''Roast thawed turkey at 325° for 20 minutes per pound.'' How many *hours* will it take to roast a 22-pound turkey?

   $7\frac{1}{3}$ hr

LESSON MASTER 2-5 A

Skills Objective B

1. Write as a product involving a negative rate. The Army Corps of Engineers expects the Mississippi River to drop 2.5 cm per day after spring floods. What is the expected drop in 14 days?

   $-2.5\frac{\text{cm}}{\text{day}} \cdot 14 \text{ days}$

2. Show that $-\frac{4}{5}$ is the reciprocal of $-\frac{5}{4}$.

   $-\frac{4}{5} \cdot -\frac{5}{4} = -1 \cdot -1 \cdot \frac{4}{5} \cdot \frac{5}{4} = 1 \cdot \frac{20}{20} = 1 \cdot 1 = 1$

In 3–11, multiply. Simplify where possible.

3. $-5 \cdot -7$ **35**   4. $-3x \cdot 2$ **$-6x$**   5. $3x \cdot -2b$ **$-6xb$**

6. $-6 \cdot \frac{2}{3} \cdot -5$ **20**   7. $2a \cdot -5a \cdot 17a$ **$-170a^3$**   8. $-\frac{2}{3} \cdot -\frac{3}{5}$ **$\frac{2}{5}$**

9. $\frac{2x}{7x} \cdot \frac{-3x}{8x}$ **$-\frac{3}{28}$**   10. $\frac{-3}{x} \cdot \frac{x}{-3}$ **1**   11. $(-5a)^2$ **$25a^2$**

12. Evaluate $2x + 3$ when $x = -5$.   **-7**

13. Evaluate $\frac{3y}{5} \cdot y$ when $y = -1$.   **$\frac{3}{5}$**

14. Evaluate $-5t^2 + 3t$ when $t = 2$.   **-14**

Properties Objective F

In 15–20, tell whether the value of the expression is positive or negative.

15. $(-1)^5$ **negative**   16. $(-3)^4$ **positive**   17. $(-3)(-2)(-5)(-\frac{1}{3})$ **positive**

18. -7^2 **negative**   19. $(-8)^9$ **negative**   20. $(11)(-4)(7)(0.01)(-6)$ **positive**

21. *Multiple choice.* Which of the following equals the opposite of x?   **d**

  (a) $1 - x$ (b) $\frac{1}{x}$ (c) $1x$ (d) $-1x$

Name _____

LESSON MASTER 2-6 A

Questions on SPUR Objectives
See pages 136-138 for objectives.

Skills Objective C

In 1–7, solve and check the equation. **Checks are not given.**

1. $\frac{1}{5}y = -12$
$y = -60$

2. $8x = 128$
$x = 16$

3. $-9a = 162$
$a = -18$

4. $\frac{3}{4}x = 15$
$x = 20$

5. $-7s = 6.3$
$s = -0.9$

6. $-\frac{5}{9} = \frac{2d}{3}$
$d = -\frac{5}{6}$

7. $20(\frac{1}{2}m) = 510$
$m = 51$

Properties Objective F

8. If you ask for a "baker's dozen" donuts, you get 13 donuts. This can be expressed as an equation: 1 baker's dozen = 13 donuts. Tell how you could apply the Multiplication Property of Equality to this equation to find out how many donuts are in 5 baker's dozens.
Sample: Multiply each side by 5.

9. Tell which property justifies each step in the solution of $80r = 200$.

Multiplicative Identity Property of 1   Multiplication Property of Equality

Associative Property of Multiplication   Property of Reciprocals

$80r = 200$
$\frac{1}{80} \cdot 80r = \frac{1}{80} \cdot 200$ **Mult. Prop. of Equality**
$(\frac{1}{80} \cdot 80)r = \frac{200}{80}$ **Assoc. Prop. of Mult.**
$1r = 25$ **Prop. of Reciprocals**
$r = 25$ **Mult. Ident. Prop. of 1**

Uses Objective H

10. The equation $p = rt$ gives the total pay for an employee who has worked t hours at r dollars per hour.

a. Use this formula to write an equation that can be used to find the hourly pay rate for an employee who earned $107 for 20 hours of work. $20r = 107$

b. Solve the equation from Part a for r.   **c.** Solve $p = rt$ for r.
$r = 5.35$ $r = \frac{p}{t}$

17

Name _____

LESSON MASTER 2-7 A

Questions on SPUR Objectives
See pages 136-138 for objectives.

Skills Objective C

In 1–6, solve and check where possible.

1. $27x = 0$ $\underset{\text{solution}}{x = 0}$ $\underset{\text{check}}{27 \cdot 0 = 0}$

2. $0a = 15$ $\underset{\text{solution}}{\text{none}}$ $\underset{\text{check}}{\text{none}}$

3. $-x = 11.5$ $\underset{\text{solution}}{x = -11.5}$ $\underset{\text{check}}{-(-11.5) = 11.5}$

4. $0y = 0$ $\underset{\text{solution}}{y = \text{all real nos.}}$ $\underset{\text{check}}{\text{Mult. Prop. of 0}}$

5. $0 = (15 - 15)t$ $\underset{\text{solution}}{t = \text{all real nos.}}$ $\underset{\text{check}}{\text{Mult. Prop. of 0}}$

6. $-(-x) = -19$ $\underset{\text{solution}}{x = -19}$ $\underset{\text{check}}{-(-(-19)) = -19}$

In 7–12, solve the equation.

7. $-\frac{1}{3}a = 20$
$a = -60$

8. $-\frac{1}{5}b = 0$
$b = 0$

9. $0c = 20$
no solutions

10. $5.3d = -0.371$
$d = -0.07$

11. $-(5.3e) = -0.371$
$e = 0.07$

12. $5.3f = 0$
$f = 0$

Properties Objective F

13. Explain why one of the equations in 7–9 doesn't have a solution.
Sample: By the Multiplication Property of Zero, $a \cdot 0 = 0$. For Question 9, the product $0c$ must equal 0, regardless of c's value.

18

Name _____

LESSON MASTER 2-8 A

Questions on SPUR Objectives
See pages 136-138 for objectives.

Skills Objective D

In 1–8, solve and check the inequality. **Sample checks are given.**

1. $15m \geq 45$
$m \geq 3$
$15 \cdot 3 = 45$
$15 \cdot 5 > 45?$
$75 > 45$

2. $60 < 12x$
$5 < x$
$60 = 12 \cdot 5$
$60 < 12 \cdot 6?$
$60 < 72$

3. $-11y > 33$
$y < -3$
$-11 \cdot -3 = 33$
$-11 \cdot -4 > 33?$
$44 > 33$

4. $54 \geq -9z$
$-6 \leq z$
$54 = -9 \cdot -6$
$54 > -9 \cdot -4?$
$54 > 36$

5. $-\frac{2}{3}n > 30$
$n < -45$
$-\frac{2}{3} \cdot -45 = 30$
$-\frac{2}{3} \cdot -48 > 30?$
$32 > 30$

6. $-\frac{9}{10} \leq \frac{3}{100}x$
$30 \geq x$
$-\frac{9}{10} = -\frac{3}{100} \cdot 30$
$-\frac{9}{10} < -\frac{3}{100} \cdot 20?$
$-\frac{9}{10} < -\frac{3}{5}$

7. $.18a \geq .09$
$a \geq .5$
$.18 \cdot .5 = .09$
$.18 \cdot .7 > .09?$
$.126 > .09$

8. $3.9b < -19.5$
$b < -5$
$3.9 \cdot -5 = -19.5$
$3.9 \cdot -6 < -19.5?$
$-23.4 < -19.5$

Properties Objective F

9. If $-x > a$, then x __?__ $-a$ $(<, >, =)$ $<$

10. What inequality results if both sides of $-\frac{2}{3}x \leq -15$ are multiplied by $-\frac{3}{2}$? $x \geq 24$

11. Explain why the opposite of a number less than 200 must be greater than -200.
Sample: Let $x < 200$. Then $-1 \cdot x > -1 \cdot 200$ by the Multiplication Property of Inequality, and $-x > -200$.

19 ▶

Name _____

▶ **LESSON MASTER 2-8 A** page 2

Uses Objective G

12. A roll of wallpaper is 1.5 ft wide and 24 ft long. At least how many rolls are needed to cover a wall that is 15 ft long and 8 ft high?

a. Write an inequality for the number of rolls of paper. $36r \geq 120$

b. Solve the inequality. $r \geq \frac{10}{3}$, or $3\frac{1}{3}$

c. Answer the question.   **at least $3\frac{1}{3}$ rolls**

Uses Objective H

13. A class has accumulated $110.50 in its party fund. How many large pizzas can the class purchase at $10.95 per pizza?

a. Write an inequality for the number of pizzas that can be purchased. $10.95p \leq 110.50$

b. Solve the inequality. $p \leq 10.09$

c. Answer the question.   **10 pizzas**

14. Mr. Johnson wants to travel at least 300 miles on the first day of his cross-country trip. How many hours must he travel if he can average 45 miles per hour?

a. Write an inequality for the number of hours he must travel. $45h \geq 300$

b. Solve the inequality. $h \geq 6\frac{2}{3}$

c. Answer the question.   **$6\frac{2}{3}$ hours or more**

20

ALGEBRA © Scott, Foresman and Company

147

LESSON MASTER 2-9 A

Questions on SPUR Objectives
See pages 136-138 for objectives.

Uses Objective I

1. A family who lives in a house in a historical district must paint their house with colors appropriate to the area in the early nineteenth century. The village permits houses of white, cream, or grey; windows of white or black; and shutters of green or black. Use a tree diagram or a list to show all ways the house could be painted.

A list is given with this order: house, windows, shutters. Colors have been abbreviated.

WWG   CWG   GWG
WWB   CWB   GWB
WBG   CBG   GBG
WBB   CBB   GBB

2. A pizzeria offers pizzas with three crust options: thin, thick, or stuffed; and four sizes: individual, small, medium, and large. How many types of pizza are possible?

12 types

3. The big breakfast at Dot's Restaurant offers diners one choice from each of the following:
   • eggs (fried, poached, scrambled, over-easy)
   • potatoes or grits
   • toast (wheat, white, or muffin)
   • meat (sausage, ham, or bacon)
   • juice (orange, grapefruit, tomato, apricot, grape, apple)
How many different big breakfasts are there?

432 breakfasts

4. A small business has its own internal phone system. Each phone number is four digits long. The first digit must be 2 to indicate an internal call, and the second digit cannot be 0. How many internal phone numbers are possible for this company?

900 numbers

---

5. Some license plates contain three letters followed by three numbers, such as MOM104 or WIN085.
   a. How many different plates are possible?

17,576,000 plates

   b. How many are there if you can't have letters repeat as the M does in MOM104?

15,600,000 plates

6. Write a problem using the Multiplication Counting Principle that has as its answer $3 \cdot 5 \cdot 2$.

Sample: How many combinations are possible if a talk show chooses one child from each family? The Chins have 3 children, the Garcias have 5, and the Andersons have 2.

7. A quiz has three multiple-choice questions, each with four options A, B, C, and D. The quiz also has five true-false questions.
   a. How many different ways are there for a student to answer the questions on the quiz?

2,048 ways

   b. How many different ways would there be for a student to answer a quiz if there were x multiple-choice questions followed by y true-false questions?

$$4^x \cdot 2^y$$

8. a. How many batting lineups can a 10-member softball team have?

3,628,800 lineups

   b. How many lineups are there if the pitcher must bat last and the best batter (who is not the pitcher) must bat fourth?

40,320 lineups

LESSON MASTER 2-10 A

Questions on SPUR Objectives
See pages 136-138 for objectives.

Vocabulary

1. Use a factorial symbol to write an expression for $8 \cdot 7 \cdot 6 \cdot 5 \cdot 4 \cdot 3 \cdot 2 \cdot 1$.

8!

Skills Objective E

2. Evaluate $n!$ when $n = 12$.
479,001,600

3. Which is larger, $5! \cdot 6!$ or $(5 \cdot 6)!$?
$(5 \cdot 6)!$

4. Explain how to simplify $\frac{50!}{48!}$ without a calculator.
$$\frac{50!}{48!} = \frac{50 \cdot 49 \cdot 48!}{48!} = 50 \cdot 49 = 2,450$$

In 5 and 6, find n.

5. $n! = 120$ **$n = 5$**

6. $n! = 40,320$ **$n = 8$**

Uses Objective I

In 7 and 8, use this information: A toy company is designing a new game that has 5 buttons of different colors. One player presses all 5 buttons in a particular order, and then his opponent must repeat the order.

7. How many orders are possible with five buttons?

120 orders

8. An advanced version of the game has 7 buttons instead of 5. How many *more* orders are possible in the advanced version?

4,920 more orders

9. Eight sprinters are running in a race. If there are no ties, in how many ways can
   a. first place be awarded? **8 ways**
   b. first and second places be awarded? **56 ways**
   c. first, second, and third places be awarded? **336 ways**
   d. all eight places be awarded? **40,320 ways**

LESSON MASTER 3-1 A

Questions on SPUR Objectives
See pages 210-213 for objectives.

Skills Objective A

In 1–4, simplify the expression.

1. $(-8 + -6) + 4$
-10

2. $-8 + (n + -21)$
$-29 + n$

3. $(x + 9) + (y + -20)$
$x + y + -11$

4. In a magic square each row, column, and diagonal has the same sum. Fill in the blanks in the square at the right so the sum is -6. **A sample is given.**

0	-10	4
2	-2	-6
-8	6	-4

Properties Objective E

In 5 and 6, tell which property of addition is illustrated.

5. $(2x + 5) + (3y + 2) = (3y + 2) + (2x + 5)$
Commutative Property of Addition

6. $8 + (2n + 9) = (8 + 2n) + 9$
Associative Property of Addition

7. Give three instances of the Associative Property of Addition.
Samples: $(1 + 9) + 2 = 1 + (9 + 2), (-2 + 3) + 5 = -2 + (3 + 5), (4 + -3) + 7 = 4 + (-3 + 7)$

Uses Objective G

In 8–10, write an addition expression or equation to describe each situation.

8. This year the company's profits were P dollars. Profits are expected to drop D dollars next year, and then increase by $5000 the following year.
$P + -D + 5000$

9. The president's popularity rating was 58% last month, but it rose r% and is now n%.
$58 + r = n$

10. Television shows are rated each week. At the beginning of the month, World-Wide news had a rating of 8.2. During the next four weeks the rating went up a points, then down b points, up 5 points, and up c points. At the end of this time, the rating reached the program's all-time high of 11.3.
$8.2 + a + -b + 5 + c = 11.3$

LESSON MASTER 3-2 A

Skills Objective A

In 1–4, simplify the expression.

1. $(4x + -12) + 12$ ___$4x$___

2. $-3.2 + (-3.2)$ ___0___

3. $-(-8x)$ ___$8x$___

4. $-15 + (3y + 15)$ ___$3y$___

Skills Objective B

In 5–10, solve and check the equation. **Checks are not given.**

5. $y + 18 = -4$
$y = -22$

6. $-4a = 628$
$a = -157$

7. $48 = n + -10$
$n = 58$

8. $y + \frac{3}{11} = \frac{8}{11}$
$y = -1$

9. $\frac{7}{8} = \frac{3}{4}m$
$m = \frac{7}{6}$, or $1\frac{1}{6}$

10. $624.5 + x = 453.9$
$x = -170.6$

Properties Objective E

In 11–13, give a. another instance of the property illustrated and b. the name of the property. **Samples are given.**

11. $-(-76) = 76$ a. ___$-(-5) = 5$___ b. ___Opp. of Opp. Prop.___

12. $0 + \frac{2}{3} = \frac{2}{3}$ a. ___$0 + -\frac{3}{4} = -\frac{3}{4}$___ b. ___Add. Ident. Prop.___

13. $\pi + (-\pi) = 0$ a. ___$7 + -7 = 0$___ b. ___Prop. of Opposites___

In 14 and 15, give the number that should be added to both sides to solve the equation quickly.

14. $82 = y + 24$ ___-24___

15. $-12 + x = 92$ ___12___

Uses Objective G

For 16 and 17, write an addition equation to describe the situation and solve the equation to answer the question.

16. During the summer of 1993 the Mississippi River flooded its banks. In St. Louis, the water was 17 feet above flood stage when it crested at 47 feet. What is considered flood stage at St. Louis?

$x + 17 = 47$ equation ___30 ft___ answer

17. The low temperature of the day occurred at 4 A.M. By 10 A.M. it had risen 12° to -9°. What was the 4 A.M. temperature?

$t + 12 = -9$ equation ___$-21°$___ answer

LESSON MASTER 3-3 A

Representations Objective I

1. a. Draw a graph for the data below, showing cars per 100 people on the horizontal axis and miles traveled per 1,000 people on the vertical axis.

COUNTRY	CARS PER 100 PEOPLE	MILES PER PERSON
United States	58	8,260
New Zealand	51	4,120
Germany	49	4,342
Canada	47	5,302
Australia	46	5,766
France	41	4,584
Austria	38	4,413
United Kingdom	38	3,881
Netherlands	36	3,731
Denmark	32	4,351
Spain	29	1,573
Japan	27	2,621
Ireland	22	4,062

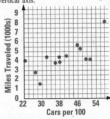

b. Describe any trend you see in the data. Are there any countries that do not follow this trend?
Sample: Countries with more cars per 100 show more miles traveled; Japan, Spain

c. If a country has 55 cars per 100 persons, estimate the distance traveled per person. **Sample: 6100 mi**

In 2–4, use this graph for 13-year-old students from six countries. For each country, a point shows the percent of students who watch 5 or more hours of TV and who do not do their homework.

2. For Canadian students, 3% don't do their homework and 19% watch 5 or more hours of TV. Which point represents Canada? ___C___

3. In the country represented by point F, about what percent of students don't do their homework? ___3%___

4. Describe any trends you see in the graph.
Sample: As the percent not doing homework increases, so does the number watching 5 + hr of TV.

LESSON MASTER 3-4 A

Representations Objective J

1. a. On the coordinate grid at the right, graph $B'A'R'K'S'$, the image of sliding pentagon $BARKS$ 2 units right and 5 units up.

b. Slide $B'A'R'K'S'$ 6 units left and 2 units up. Label the image $B''A''R''K''S''$.

c. Use your answer to Part b to find the coordinates of point B''.
___$(-5, 6)$___

d. Point $B = (-1, -1)$. Explain how to find the coordinates of point B'' without drawing $B'A'R'K'S'$ and $B''A''R''K''S''$.
Sample: Add (2 + -6), or -4, to the x-coordinate and (5 + 2), or 7, to the y-coordinate.

2. The point $(7, -4)$ is translated 2 units left and 1 unit down. What are the coordinates of the image? ___$(5, -5)$___

In 3 and 4, give the image of point $Q = (x, y)$ under a slide

3. 3 units right and 5 units down.
$Q' = (x + 3, y + -5)$

4. 9 units left.
$Q' = (x + -9, y)$

In 5–7, give a formula for a slide for which the image of the point $(-4, -1)$ will be **Samples are given.**

5. in Quadrant II. ___up 7 units___

6. in Quadrant IV. ___right 8 units___

7. on the y-axis. ___right 4 units___

In 8–10, use the graph at the right. It shows P and P', its image under a slide.

8. Describe the slide: ___?___ units to the (left or right) and ___?___ units (up or down).
___1, right___ ___3, down___

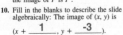

9. Point J is shown on the graph. Plot J', its image under the same slide under which the image of P is P'.

10. Fill in the blanks to describe the slide algebraically: The image of (x, y) is $(x + $ ___1___ $, y + $ ___-3___ $)$.

LESSON MASTER 3-5 A

Skills Objective B

In 1–6, solve and check the equation.

1. $-12x + 2 = 50$
$x = -4$
$-12 \cdot -4 + 2 = 50?$
$50 = 50$

2. $-20 = 2n$
$n = -10$
$-20 = 2 \cdot -10?$
$-20 = -20$

3. $-4 + \frac{5}{6}a = -31$
$a = -42$
$-4 + \frac{5}{6} \cdot -42 = -31?$
$-31 = -31$

4. $144 = 18k + -54$
$k = 11$
$144 = 18 \cdot 11$
$+ -54?$
$144 = 144$

5. $-28a = 63$
$a = -2.25$
$-28 \cdot -2.25 = 63?$
$63 = 63$

6. $.03y + 1.2 = -6.3$
$y = -250$
$.03 \cdot -250 + 1.2$
$= -6.3?$
$-6.3 = -6.3$

Uses Objective G

7. For a school sale, Janine made several batches of cookies, with about 60 cookies per batch. Other students contributed 350 cookies. Altogether there were 650 cookies for the sale. How many batches did Janine make? ___5 batches___

8. Pedro ordered x boxes of paper at $25.89 per box and a printer ribbon which cost $7.29. The total for the order was $214.41. How many boxes of paper were ordered? Write an equation to describe this situation. Then solve the equation to find the answer.

$25.89x + 7.29 = 214.41$ equation ___8 boxes___ answer

Representations Objective K

9.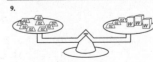

a. What equation is pictured by the diagram at the left?
___$9 = 3w + 3$___

b. What is the weight of one box?
___2 oz___

10. a. Sketch a balance-scale diagram for $4w + 1 = 13$.

b. What is the solution to the equation? ___$w = 3$___

■ = w ▲ = oz weights

LESSON MASTER 3-6 A

Questions on SPUR Objectives
See pages 210-213 for objectives.

Vocabulary

1. Give an example of *like terms*.
Sample: $3x$, $-7x$

2. Give an example of *unlike terms*.
Sample: $5x^2$, $4y$

Skills Objective A

In 3–8, simplify the expression.

3. $12n + 18n$
$30n$

4. $8x(5x) + 12x^2$
$52x^2$

5. $5a + 2b + 3b + -8a$
$-3a + 5b$

6. $y + y + 3$
$2y + 3$

7. $(4n^2 + 9) + (-3n^2 + 4)$
$n^2 + 13$

8. $4(11x) + 21x$
$65x$

Skills Objective B

9. Solve and check $10n + -8n = 622$.
$n = 311$; $3110 + -2488 = 622$

Properties Objective E

In 10–11, tell what property has been applied.

10. $a + a = 1a + 1a$
Mult. Ident. Prop. of 1

11. $\frac{3}{5}x + \frac{1}{5}x = \frac{4}{5}x$
Distr. Prop.

Uses Objective G

12. Each week Maria earns \$8 more than Dave at the store where they work. Their total pay for the week will be \$60. Write and solve an equation for this situation to find each person's pay.
$(D + 8) + D = 60$ Maria: \$34; Dave: \$26
equation   answer

Representations Objective K

13. a. What is the area of the left rectangle?
$15x$

b. What is the area of the right rectangle?
$4x$

c. Give the total area of the largest rectangle in simplified form.
$19x$

15   4

29

LESSON MASTER 3-7 A

Questions on SPUR Objectives
See pages 210-213 for objectives.

Skills Objective A

In 1–6, simplify the expression.

1. $4(x + y + 8)$
$4x + 4y + 32$

2. $n(n - 12)$
$n^2 - 12n$

3. $10a(3a - 8)$
$30a^2 - 80a$

4. $-2(x + 15) + 4$
$-2x + -26$

5. $9x + 15x - 4$
$24x - 4$

6. $-6(n + 1) + (11n + 1)$
$5n + -5$

Skills Objective B

In 7–10, solve the equation and check your result.

7. $2.4 = 6(n - 1.3)$
$n = 1.7$
$2.4 = 6(1.7 - 1.3)$?
$2.4 = 2.4$

8. $8(2x + 5) - 16 = 72$
$x = 3$
$8(2 \cdot 3 + 5) - 16 = 72$?
$72 = 72$

9. $\frac{3}{4}(3x + 8) = 15$
$x = 4$
$\frac{3}{4}(3 \cdot 4 + 8) = 15$?
$15 = 15$

10. $4(1.5y + -7) + 2y = -4$
$y = 3$
$4(1.5 \cdot 3 + -7) + 2 \cdot 3 = -4$?
$-4 = -4$

Properties Objective E

In 11–13, tell whether the Distributive Property has been applied in the equation. Write *yes* or *no*.

11. $3y + 8y + 4 = 11y + 4$
yes

12. $9(8 + 2x) + 3 = 3 + 9(8 + 2x)$
no

13. $4(2a + b + 5c) = 8a + 4b + 20c$
yes

30 ▶

Properties Objective F

14. Sam's regular rate of pay is \$6.20 per hour. If he is paid time and a half for overtime, what is his overtime rate of pay? Explain how you can mentally compute your answer.
\$9.30 per hour; sample explanation:
$1\frac{1}{2} \times 6.20 = 1(6.20) + \frac{1}{2}(6.20) = 6.20 + 3.10 = 9.30$

15. The freshman class has 99 students. Mentally compute the cost if the entire class buys

a. T-shirts at \$8 each. $8(99) = 8(100 - 1)$
\$792

b. yearbooks at \$20 each. $20(99) = 20(100 - 1)$
\$1980

Representations Objective K

In 16 and 17, express the area of each largest rectangle as **a.** length times width and **b.** the sum of areas of smaller rectangles.

16.

5

x
y
z

a. $5(x + y + z)$
b. $5x + 5y + 5z$

17.

4

x   5

a. $4(x + 5)$
b. $4x + 20$

31

LESSON MASTER 3-8 A

Questions on SPUR Objectives
See pages 210-213 for objectives.

Uses Objective H

In 1–9, use the sequence of designs shown below.

1. Draw the next design in the sequence.

1st   2nd   3rd   4th

2. Complete the chart at the right to show the perimeters of the first through fifth designs.

Design Number	Perimeter
1	16
2	20
3	24
4	28
5	32

3. If the perimeter of a figure is 84, what would the perimeter of the next design be?
88

4. If $n =$ the design number and $p =$ the perimeter, then the relationship between them is described by $p = 12 + 4n$.

a. Find the perimeter of the 15th design.
72

b. Which design has a perimeter of 140?
32nd

5. Complete the chart at the right.

n (Design Number)	s (Number of Squares)
1	7
2	9
3	11
4	13
5	15

6. If one design has 49 squares, how many squares will the next design have?
51 squares

7. Fill in the blanks in the equation to make a formula for this pattern.
$s = 5 + 2 n$

8. How many squares would then be in the 12th design?
29 squares

9. Which design is made up of 59 squares?
27th

In 10–12, use the salad price list at the right.

Salad Weight	Price
1 oz	\$ .65
2 oz	\$ .90
3 oz	\$1.15
4 oz	\$1.40
5 oz	\$1.65

10. How much would a 6-oz salad cost?
\$1.90

11. How does the price change as the weight increases?
Sample: for each 1-oz increase, the price increases by \$.25.

12. Write an equation for the cost of a salad that weighs w oz.
$s = .40 + .25w$

32

Name _____

LESSON MASTER 3-9 A

Questions on SPUR Objectives
See pages 210-213 for objectives.

Skills Objective C

In 1–4, find the sum.

1. $-\frac{6}{7} + \frac{11}{7}$ $\dfrac{5}{7}$

2. $6\frac{3}{4} + \frac{3}{4}$ $7\frac{1}{2}$

3. $\frac{5}{3n} + \frac{-25}{3n} + \frac{-4}{3n}$ $\dfrac{-8}{n}$

4. $\frac{3n+8}{4} + \frac{n+3}{4}$ $\dfrac{4n+11}{4}$

5. What common denominator would you use to add $\frac{a}{10}$ and $\frac{5a}{4}$?   **Sample: 20**

In 6–9, use a common denominator to write as a single fraction.

6. $\frac{x}{10} + \frac{8x}{5}$ $\dfrac{17x}{10}$

7. $n + \frac{n}{4}$ $\dfrac{5n}{4}$

8. $\frac{-2y}{15} + \frac{5y}{y}$ $\dfrac{7y}{10}$

9. $5a + \frac{2a}{7}$ $\dfrac{37a}{7}$

10. Simplify $\frac{-3}{8}x + \frac{1}{4}x$. $\dfrac{-1}{8}x$

In 11–13, use this sequence: $\frac{1}{10}, \frac{1}{5}, \frac{3}{10}, \frac{2}{5}, \frac{1}{2}, \frac{3}{5}, \frac{7}{10}, \frac{4}{5}, \frac{9}{10}, 1$

11. What is the difference between each term and the term which precedes it? $\dfrac{1}{10}$

12. Write the next ten terms in the sequence. $\frac{11}{10}, \frac{6}{5}, \frac{13}{10}, \frac{7}{5}, \frac{3}{2}, \frac{8}{5}, \frac{17}{10}, \frac{9}{5}, \frac{19}{10}, 2$

13. Describe any patterns you see in the sequence.
Samples: every 10th term is an integer; even-numbered terms have a denominator of 5 and their numerators are consecutive integers.

Properties Objective E

In 14–16, simplify the sum. Tell whether you used the Distributive Property for Adding Fractions. Write yes or no.

14. $\frac{a}{c} + \frac{b}{c}$ $\dfrac{a+b}{c}$ **yes**

15. $\frac{4}{5} + \left(x + \frac{-4}{5}\right)$ **x**   **no**

16. $\frac{5x}{3} + \frac{2x}{3}$ $\dfrac{7x}{3}$ **yes**

33

Name _____

LESSON MASTER 3-10 A

Questions on SPUR Objectives
See pages 210-213 for objectives.

Vocabulary

1. How is the Addition Property of Inequality different from the Multiplication Property of Inequality?
Sample: Adding a negative number to both sides does not change the sense of the inequality, but multiplying both sides by a negative number does.

Skills Objective D

2. Chuck solved $-5x + 8 < -47$. His solution was $x < 11$. Chuck did not check his answer, so he did not realize that his answer was wrong.
   $-5 \cdot 11 + 8 = -47$

a. Write a check to show that his answer is wrong.

b. Write a note to explain to Chuck what he did wrong.
Sample: When you multiplied both sides by $-\frac{1}{5}$, you forgot to change the sense of the inequality.

In 3–6, solve each inequality and check your result.   **Sample checks are given.**

3. $-2y + 8 \geq 26$
$y \leq -9$
$-2 \cdot -9 + 8 = 26$
$-2 \cdot -10 + 8 > 26?$
$28 > 26$

4. $-2 + 8n \geq 26$
$n \geq 3.5$
$-2 + 8 \cdot 3.5 = 26$
$-2 + 8 \cdot 4 > 26?$
$30 > 26$

5. $-6 < -n + 9$
$n < 15$
$-6 = -15 + 9$
$-6 < 0 + 9?$
$-6 < 9$

6. $4(\frac{1}{2}x + 17) \leq 164$
$x \leq 48$
$4(\frac{1}{2} \cdot 48 + 17) = 164$
$4(\frac{1}{2} \cdot 40 + 17) < 164?$
$148 < 164$

Uses Objective G

7. For the last thirty days Al's Auto's sold an average of C cars each day and broke the previous record of 484 cars sold in 30 days.

a. Write an inequality to describe this situation. $30C \geq 485$

b. On the average, how many cars were sold each day during the last 30 days?   **more than 16 cars**

34   ▶

Name _____

8. When the temperature is $T°$ Fahrenheit, a certain type of tree cricket chirps about C times per minute, and $T = \frac{1}{4}C + 37$. Yesterday's temperature stayed below 90°F. How fast were crickets chirping?
less than 212 chirps per min

Representations Objective K

9.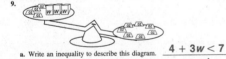

a. Write an inequality to describe this diagram. $4 + 3w < 7$

b. Solve the inequality from Part a. $w < 1$

Representations Objective L

10. *Multiple choice.* Which of the graphs below shows the solutions of $-3x + 8 < 38$?   **b**

(a) ◀———○———▶ x
     10

(b) ◀———○———▶ x
     -10

(c) ◀———●———▶ x
     -10

(d) ◀———●———▶ x
     10

In 11–13, graph all solutions.

11. $2.4n + -1.8 > -4.2$ $n > -1$

◀——┬——┬——┬——○——┬——┬——┬——┬——┬——┬——▶
-4   -3   -2   -1   0   1   2   3   4   5   6

12. $16 > -2x + 30$ $x > 7$

◀——┬——┬——┬——┬——┬——┬——┬——○——┬——┬——▶ x
0   1   2   3   4   5   6   7   8   9   10

13. $\frac{3}{5}x + 15 \leq 90$ $x \leq 125$

◀——┬——————●——————┬——————┬——————┬——▶ x
100   125   150   175   200

35

Name _____

LESSON MASTER 4-1 A

Questions on SPUR Objectives
See pages 278-281 for objectives.

Skills Objective A

In 1–6, simplify the expression.

1. $3 - -25$ **-28**

2. $-8 - 10$ **-18**

3. $4x + 3x - 8x$ **-x**

4. $15y - -y$ **16y**

5. $\frac{5}{8}t - \frac{1}{2}t - \frac{3}{8}t$ $-\frac{1}{4}t$

6. $\frac{-6n}{x} - \frac{5n}{x}$ $\dfrac{-11n}{x}$

7. Evaluate $x^2 - y$ when $x = -6$ and $y = -1$.   **37**

8. Evaluate $5 - 10 + 15 - 20 + 25 - 30 + \ldots + 95 - 100$.   **-50**

9. Let S = the amount of money Scrooge has and M = the amount of money Midas has. If $S - M < 0$, which man has more money? Explain how you know.
Midas; sample: Solve the inequality $S - M < 0$ for S; then $S < M$.

Properties Objective E

In 10–13, use this table showing a person's weight from week to week. The numbers in the Change row show how the weight compares to the weight the previous week. Complete the table.

Week	1	2	3	4	5	6
Weight	178	175	176	172	174	177
Change		-3	1	10. ?	11. ?	12. ?

10. **-4**   11. **2**   12. **3**

13. How could you find the change for Week 2

a. using subtraction?   **Subtract 178 from 175.**

b. using addition?   **Add -178 to 175.**

In 14–16, rewrite each subtraction as an addition.

14. $-3 - 5 + n$ $-3 + -5 + n$

15. $6 + 11 - -30$ $6 + 11 + 30$

16. $5x - 12 - -7y$ $5x + -12 + 7y$

36

LESSON MASTER 4-2 A

Uses Objective H

In 1–3, use the table at the right. Remember that a negative profit is a loss.

Profits for World-Wide Widget (in millions)

DOMESTIC		FOREIGN	
Factory A:	13.2	Factory E:	-6.4
Factory B:	8.6	Factory F:	-1.3
Factory C:	-1.9	Factory G:	-15.0
Factory D:	.4		

1. How much more did the most profitable factory earn than the least profitable?
   28.2 million

2. What was the range of earnings for the domestic factories?
   15.1 million

3. What was the range of earnings for the foreign factories?
   13.7 million

4. Let K = Kendra's age and M = Marsha's age. Kendra is younger than Marsha. Which is positive, $M − K$ or $K − M$? **$M − K$**

In 5 and 6, let R = Ryan's age now. Write an expression for Ryan's age

5. 8 years ago. **$R − 8$**

6. 3 years from now. **$R + 3$**

In 7 and 8, write a subtraction expression for the length of the segment marked with a question mark (?).

7.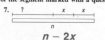
   $n − 2x$

8.
   $2y − 3a$

9. Home-Bake Bread launched a new advertising campaign and is keeping track of the number of loaves sold.

Week 1	2,452
Week 2	3,621
Week 3	4,102
Week 4	3,015

   a. What was the change from Week 2 to Week 3? **481 loaves**

   b. What was the change from Week 3 to Week 4? **-1,087 loaves**

In 10 and 11 let A = Alissa's age. Steve's age is $A − 11$ and Beth's age is $A + 4$.

10. Arrange the three ages in order from youngest to oldest. **$A − 11 \quad A \quad A + 4$**

11. The oldest person is y years older than the youngest. Find the value of y and explain your reasoning.

   $y = 15$; sample: $A + 4 − (A − 11) = 15$, so the oldest person is 15 years older than the youngest.

LESSON MASTER 4-3 A

Skills Objective B

In 1–6, solve and check the equation. **Checks are not given.**

1. $8x − 13 = 51$
   $x = 8$

2. $1.5 = -1.2n − 0.9$
   $n = 2$

3. $6 − y = -20$
   $y = 26$

4. $\frac{3}{7}b − 9 = 2$
   $b = \frac{77}{3}$

5. $3(22v − 1) = 162$
   $v = 2.5$

6. $-6(m + 2) + 4 = 36$
   $m = -\frac{22}{3}$

Skills Objective C

7. *Skill sequence.* Solve.
   a. $5x − 40 = 125$ $x = 33$
   b. $5x − 40 < 125$ $x < 33$
   c. $5 − 40x = 125$ $x = -3$
   d. $5 − 40x < 125$ $x > -3$

In 8–10, a. solve and b. graph.

8. $-8 ≤ 4d − 26$
   a. $d ≥ 4.5$
   b. (4, 4.5, 5)

9. $15 + 2(5z − 50) < 68$
   a. $z < 15.3$
   b. (15.2, 15.3, 15.4)

10. $9n − 54 > -36$
    a. $n > 2$
    b. (1, 2, 3)

Uses Objectives H and I

In 11–13, write an equation or an inequality to describe the situation. Then answer the question.

11. Suppose the temperature started at 10° and dropped 4° each hour. After x hours it was -14°. How many hours had elapsed?
    $10 − 4x = -14$ (sentence)   **6 hours** (answer)

12. When a certain number is multiplied by 12 and then the product is subtracted from 21, the answer is -63. What is the number?
    $21 − 12n = -63$ (sentence)   **7** (answer)

13. Of the 478 people who started the race, quite a few dropped out and fewer than 350 crossed the finish line. How many people dropped out?
    $478 − x < 350$ (sentence)   **at least 129 people** (answer)

LESSON MASTER 4-4 A

Representations Objective K

In 1–4, use the spreadsheet at the right. It shows weather data for an afternoon.

	A	B	C
1	TIME	TEMP	RAIN
2	1	87	0
3	2	88	0
4	3	88	.5
5	4	84	1.2
6	5	79	.1
7	6	77	0
8			

1. What is in cell C3?
   0

2. Which cell contains the number 79?
   cell B6

3. Suppose that the formula =C2+C3+C4+C5+C6+C7 is entered in cell C8.
   a. What value will appear in cell C8? **1.8**
   b. What real-life quantity does this formula calculate? **total amount of rain**

4. What formula can be entered in cell B8 to find the average temperature for the afternoon?
   =(B2+B3+B4+B5+B6+B7)/6

In 5–8, use this information: Subscribers to the *Midvale Times* can have the paper delivered each day for $4.00 per week or on Sundays only for $1.25 per week. The spreadsheet below shows the number and type of subscriptions for the four areas of town.

	A	B	C	D
1	ROUTE	DAILY	SUNDAY ONLY	WEEKLY $
2	north	128	34	554.50
3	east	161	45	700.25
4	south	103	21	438.25
5	west	115	28	
6	total	507	128	

5. What formula can be used in cell C6 to calculate the total number of subscribers who get the Sunday paper only?
   =C2+C3+C4+C5

▶ **LESSON MASTER 4-4 A** *page 2*

6. a. What formula can be entered in cell D5 to find the total cost for the papers delivered in the western route?
   =B5*4+C5*1.25

   b. What number will appear in cell D5? **495.00**

7. Give two different formulas that could be entered in cell D6 to give the total cost for all four routes.
   =D2+D3+D4+D5   **=B6*4+C6*1.25**

8. If the east route increases to 165 daily subscriptions so that 165 is in cell B3, which other cells would change?
   cells B6, D3, and D6

In 9 and 10, use the spreadsheet below. Barb uses it to keep track of her money. She has columns for her weekly allowance, her pay for mowing lawns, and baby-sitting, and her weekly expenses.

	A	B	C	D	E	F
1	START	ALLOWANCE	MOW LAWNS	BABYSIT	SPENDING	END
2	48.15	5.00	15.00	3.25	4.88	66.52
3	66.52	5.00	10.00	0.00	12.92	68.60
4	68.60	5.00	10.00	6.50	43.21	46.89

9. Write a formula for cell F2 which finds Barb's balance at the end of the week.
   =A2+B2+C2+D2−E2

10. Barb decides to add a column to show how the amount she has changes from week to week.
    a. If cell G3 contains the formula =F3−F2, what number will appear in cell G3? **2.08**
    b. If cell G4 contains the formula =F4−F3, what number will appear in cell G4? **-21.71**
    c. Why do the answers to Parts a and b have different signs?
       Row 3 shows that Barb spent less than she took in; Row 4 shows that she spent more.

11. In a spreadsheet, suppose cell B9 contains the number 28 and cell C9 contains the number 6. If cell G9 contains the formula =(B9−2*C9)^2, what number will appear in cell G9? **256**

LESSON MASTER 4-5 A

Questions on SPUR Objectives
See pages 278-281 for objectives.

Skills Objective D

1. *Multiple choice.* Which expression is *not* equal to $-(8x - 10)$?　**a**
(a) $-8x - 10$　　　(b) $-8x - -10$
(c) $-8x + 10$　　　(d) $-2(4x - 5)$

2. Juan simplified $-6(2x - 4)$ and got $-12x - 24$. Write a note to Juan to convince him that his answer is wrong by substituting 3 for x in both expressions.
Sample: If you substitute 3 for x in both expressions, you get $-6(2 \cdot 3 - 4) = -12$ and $-12 \cdot 3 - 24 = -60$. So, $-6(2x - 4) \neq -12x - 24$.

In 3–10, simplify the expression.

3. $-2(-2x + 25)$　　**4.** $-3(n - 2x + 11)$　　**5.** $-24k - (4k + 3)$
　$4x - 50$　　　　　$-3n + 6x - 33$　　　　$-28k - 3$

6. $(5a + 9) - (4a - 2)$　**7.** $(2y - 16) - (y + 8)$　**8.** $6n - 4(n + 1)$
　$a + 11$　　　　　　$y - 24$　　　　　　$2n - 44$

9. $\frac{3a}{4} - \frac{5a - 8}{12}$　　　　**10.** $\frac{x + 4}{5} - \frac{x + 5}{6} - \frac{5 - x}{3}$
　$\frac{a + 2}{3}$　　　　　　　　$\frac{11x - 51}{30}$

In 11–14, solve and check the equation.

11. $9x - (3 + 5x) = 17$
$x = 5$
$9 \cdot 5 - (3 + 5 \cdot 5) = 17?$
　　　$17 = 17$

12. $50 = -5(3x + 8) - (7x - 24)$
$x = -3$
$50 = -5(3 \cdot -3 + 8)$
　$- (7 \cdot -3 - 24)?$
$50 = 50$

13. $20 - 2(x + 41) = -38$
$x = -12$
$20 - 2(-12 + 41) = -38?$
　　　$-38 = -38$

14. $-4(x + 8) + 3x = 47$
$x = -79$
$-4(-79 + 8) + 3 \cdot -79$
　　　$= 47?$
　　　$47 = 47$

41

LESSON MASTER 4-6 A

Questions on SPUR Objectives
See pages 278-281 for objectives.

Representations Objective L

1. Yvonne is 2 years younger than her sister Xandra. Let Yvonne's age be y and Xandra's age be x.

a. Which equation describes this situation, $y = x + 2$ or $y = x - 2$?　　**$y = x - 2$**

b. Fill in the chart with some possible ages for the girls.

Xandra x	Yvonne y	Ordered Pairs (x, y)
5	3	(5, 3)
6	4	(6, 4)
7	5	(7, 5)
8	6	(8, 6)
9	7	(9, 7)
10	8	(10, 8)

c. Graph possible pairs of ages for the girls.

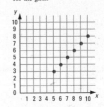

d. How old were the girls when the sum of their ages was 16?
　　　9 and 7

2. Consider the equation $x + y = 7$.

a. Write four pairs (x, y) that satisfy $x + y = 7$.

x	y	(x, y)
-2	9	(-2, 9)
0	7	(0, 7)
4	3	(4, 3)
7	0	(7, 0)

b. Graph *all* ordered pairs satisfying the equation on the grid at the right.
Sample points are given.

42

LESSON MASTER 4-7 A

Questions on SPUR Objectives
See pages 278-281 for objectives.

Properties Objective F

1. Use a protractor and the angle at the right.

a. Find its measure.　**35°**

b. Draw a complement.　$\angle ABC$

c. Draw a supplement.　$\angle DBE$

In 2–4, the measure of an angle is given. Find the measure of **a.** a complement and **b.** a supplement.

2. 18°　**a.** **72°**
　　　b. **162°**

3. 124°　**a.** **none**
　　　b. **56°**

4. $g°$　**a.** **$(90 - g)°$**
　　　b. **$(180 - g)°$**

5. a. Write an equation to describe the situation shown in the diagram.
$(5x + 2) + (20x + 3) = 180$

b. Find the value of x.　**$x = 7$**　**c.** m $\angle ABC =$　**143°**

6. Let $x =$ the measure of $\angle A$. The measure of $\angle B$ is 6 more than three times the measure of $\angle A$. $\angle A$ and $\angle B$ are complements. Write and solve an equation to find the measure of each angle.
$x + (3x + 6) = 90$　　$m\angle A = 21°, m\angle B = 69°$
　　equation　　　　　　　　answer

7. Write an expression to represent the measure of $\angle GEM$ in terms of a and b.
Sample: $180 - a - b$

8. Use the triangle at the right.

a. Write an equation relating the angles.
$(y + 14) + (2y - 10) + (y - 20) = 180$

b. Find the value of y.　**$y = 49$**

c. Find the measures of the angles.　**63°, 88°, 29°**

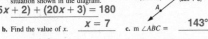

9. In the triangle at the right, label each unlabeled angle with its measure.

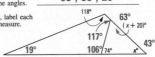

43

LESSON MASTER 4-8 A

Questions on SPUR Objectives
See pages 278-281 for objectives.

Properties Objective G

In 1–3, write an expression for the length of $\overline{BC}$ in terms of x and y.

1.　**$x - y$**　　**2.**　**$x + y$**　　**3.**　**$y - x$**

4. Fill in the blanks. Use the triangle at the right.

a. $x <$ **$\frac{19 + 15, \text{ or } 34}{4}$**　**b.** $x >$ **$\frac{19 - 15, \text{ or } 4}{34}$**

c. **4** $< x <$ **34**

5. Suppose you know that in $\triangle PET$, $PE = 29.6$ and $ET = 21.8$. The length of $\overline{PT}$ is between what two numbers?　**7.8 and 51.4**

6. Give an example of three numbers that *cannot* be the lengths of the sides of a triangle.　**Sample: 2, 7, 11**

7.　Refer to the triangle at the left. Fill in the blanks with simplified expressions.
$a + 23$ $< PQ <$ **$7a + 19$**

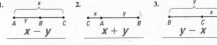
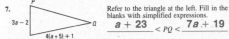

Uses Objective J

8. Millford is 83 miles from Rockton and Milford is 130 miles from Portland. Is it possible that Rockton is 210 miles from Portland? Explain why or why not.
Yes; The numbers satisfy the Triangle Inequality; $83 + 130 > 210$, $83 + 210 > 130$, $210 + 130 > 83$

9. It takes Rhonda 15 minutes to walk to Amber's house and 24 minutes to walk to Tanya's house. Assuming Amber and Rhonda walk at the same speed, how long would it take Amber to walk to Tanya's house?　**between 9 and 39 min**

44

153

LESSON MASTER 4-9 A

Questions on SPUR Objectives
See pages 278-281 for objectives.

Representations Objective L

In 1–3, use these charges for Pat's pizza: $6 for a basic pizza, plus $1 for every topping that is ordered.

1. a. Fill in the table showing the number of toppings t and the cost of the pizza c.

Toppings t	Cost c	(t, c)
0	6	(0, 6)
1	7	(1, 7)
2	8	(2, 8)
3	9	(3, 9)
4	10	(4, 10)
5	11	(5, 11)

b. Graph the ordered pairs (t, c) on the grid below.

c. Write an equation that represents c in terms of t.

$$c = 6 + t$$

d. What would be a suitable domain for this graph?

whole numbers less than 12

In 2 and 3, Pat's plans for increasing her profit are given. For each plan, fill in the table, make a graph, and write an equation for the graph. Then describe how the graph is different from the first graph.

2. Plan A: Raise the basic pizza charge to $8, but continue to charge $1 for each topping.

Toppings t	Cost c	(t, c)
0	8	(0, 8)
1	9	(1, 9)
2	10	(2, 10)
3	11	(3, 11)
4	12	(4, 12)
5	13	(5, 13)

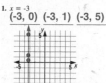

equation: $c = 8 + t$

differences from first graph: Sample: The graph is what you would get if you shifted the first graph up 2 units.

45 ►

---

3. Plan B: Keep the basic charge at $6, but charge $1.50 for each topping.

Toppings t	Cost c	(t, c)
0	6	(0, 6)
1	7.50	(1, 7.5)
2	9	(2, 9)
3	10.50	(3, 10.5)
4	12	(4, 12)
5	13.50	(5, 13.5)

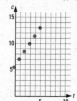

equation: $c + 6 + 1.5t$

differences from first graph: Sample: The graphs start at the same place, but this one is steeper.

4. The temperature was -1°, but it was dropping 3° each hour.

a. Complete the table.

Hours h	Temperature t
0	-1
1	-4
2	-7
3	-10

b. Graph the situation below.

c. Write an equation to describe the temperature in terms of the number of hours that have passed.

$$t = -1 - 3h$$

5. Consider the equation $y = -2x + 7$.

a. Make a table of four pairs of values that satisfy the equation.

b. Graph the equation at the right.

x	y
-1	9
0	7
3	1
5	-3

Sample points are given.

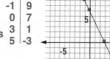

46

LESSON MASTER 5-1 A

Questions on SPUR Objectives
See pages 343-346 for objectives.

Representations Objective H

In 1 and 2, an equation is given. **a.** Give the coordinates of three points that satisfy the equation. **b.** Graph the equation.

Sample points are given.

1. $x = -3$

(-3, 0) (-3, 1) (-3, 5)

2. $y = 5$

(-1, 5) (-4, 5) (3, 5)

In 3–5, graph the given line and the point (2, 5). Tell where (2, 5) lies in relation to the line: *on, above, below, to the left,* or *to the right.*

3. $y = -1$ **4.** $x = 2$ **5.** $x = 5$

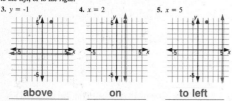

above   on   to left

In 6–10, give an equation for the line shown or described.

6.

$$y = 2$$

7.

$$x = 4$$

47 ►

---

8. the vertical line through (-5, 1) $x = -5$

9. the horizontal line through (0, -8) $y = -8$

10. the line through (-3, 5), (0, -5), and $(\frac{1}{3}, -5)$ $y = -5$

Representations Objective I

11. The Gomez family has bought a collie puppy which weighs 23 pounds. The puppy is expected to gain 2 pounds per week. Full-grown collies typically weight about 65 pounds.

a. Write an equation to describe the puppy's weight y after x weeks.

$$y = 23 + 2x$$

b. Graph your equation from Part a on the grid at the right.

c. Graph $y = 65$ to represent the final expected weight of the puppy on the grid at the right.

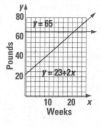

d. Use the graph to approximate when the puppy will weigh 65 pounds.

at 21 weeks

e. Check your answer to Part d by solving an equation. $23 + 2x = 65; x = 21$

In 12–14, use this information: Megan has decided to start lifting weights. Now she can curl 10 pounds and she feels she can increase this by 2.5 pounds each month if she works out regularly. This is shown on the graph below.

12. Draw a horizontal line showing where the weight is 17.5 pounds.

13. Write an inequality to describe the number of months x during which Megan can curl no more than 17.5 pounds. $x < 3$

14. Write an inequality to describe when she can curl more than 15 pounds. $x > 2$

48

LESSON MASTER 5-2 A

Representations Objective G

1. In the week before the election for mayor, the voters who had been undecided were finally choosing between the two candidates. According to poll results, Schultz, who started the week with 47,000 votes, began gaining 450 votes each day. Chen, who started with 44,900, began gaining 800 votes a day.

DAY	SCHULTZ	CHEN
1	47,000	44,900
2	47,450	45,700
3	47,900	46,500
4	48,350	47,300
5	48,800	48,100
6	49,250	48,900
7 Elec. Day	49,700	49,700

a. Fill in the chart at the right.

b. Who should be expected to win the election?
It was tied.

c. Write an equation for Schultz's votes S in terms of the day number d.
$$S = 47,000 + 450(d - 1)$$

d. Write an equation for Chen's votes C in terms of the day number d.
$$C = 44,900 + 800(d-1)$$

e. What equation could be solved to estimate when the two candidates were tied?
$$47,000 + 450(d - 1) = 44,900 + 800(d - 1)$$

2. Yuriko has been offered two jobs. Mendoza, Inc., pays $25,000 per year at first, but each year she will get an $800 raise. Consolidated Industries pays $28,000 now, but yearly raises are only $300. Yuriko made a spreadsheet to help her choose between the two jobs.

a. What formula could be used in cell C3?
$$=C2+300$$

b. What formula could be used in cell C4?
$$=C3+300$$

	A	B	C
1	YEAR	MENDOZA	CONSOLIDATED
2	1	25,000	28,000
3	2	25,800	28,300
4	3	26,600	28,600
5	4	27,400	28,900
6	5	28,200	29,200
7	6	29,000	29,500
8	7	29,800	29,800
9	8	30,600	30,100
10	9	31,400	30,400
11	10	32,200	30,700

c. Complete the spreadsheet.

d. How does the pay for the jobs compare over a 10-year period?
Sample: By the 10th year, Mendoza is paying more; the total amount is more for Consolidated.

49

LESSON MASTER 5-3 A

Skills Objective A

1.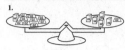

a. Write the equation represented by this drawing.
$$w + 9 = 5w + 1$$

b. Solve the equation to find the weight w of one box.
2 oz

In 2-7, solve each equation and check the result.
Checks are not shown.

2. $x + 50 = 2x + 100$
$x = -50$

3. $9n = 4n - 35$
$n = -7$

4. $1.2 - .4y = .6y + 4.2$
$y = -3$

5. $3(2x + 4) + 2 = 4x + 50$
$x = 18$

6. $C = \frac{9}{5}C + 32$
$C = -40$

7. $4(6 - 3y) = 2(15y + 12)$
$y = 0$

Properties Objective E

In 8 and 9, tell what should be done to both sides of the equation first in order to solve.

8. $13x + 5 = -9x - 1$
Add 9x or -13x.

9. $5y + 3 = 13y$
Add -5y or -13y.

Uses Objective F

11. A club sponsored a concert. The income from the concert came from a $250 donation by the school activity fund and ticket sales at $8 per ticket. Rent for an auditorium was $200. The band was paid $1400 plus $2 for each ticket sold. Since the income was exactly equal to expenses, the club just broke even and did not make money. Let x = the number of tickets sold.

a. Write an expression for the income.
$$250 + 8x$$

b. Write an expression for the expenses.
$$200 + 1400 + 2x$$

c. Write an equation that says the income and expenses were equal.
$$250 + 8x = 1600 + 2x$$

d. How many tickets were sold?
225 tickets

50

LESSON MASTER 5-4 A

Uses Objective F
Representations Objective I

1. The graph below shows estimated populations of two towns in t years.

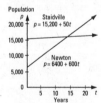

Population
P
20,000 — Staidville $p = 15,200 + 50t$
15,000
10,000 — Newton $p = 6400 + 600t$
5,000
0 — 5 10 15 20 t
Years

a. Use an equation to estimate in how many years the populations will be equal. Use the graph to check your answer.
16 years

b. For what values of t is Newton's estimated population less?
$$t < 16$$

c. When is Newton's estimated population greater?
$$t > 16$$

2. A gas station that normally sells gasoline for $1.29 per gallon is offering the special deal advertised at the right. Let g = gallons of gas purchased and c = cost.

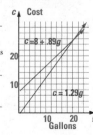
Bargain Special
Gas only $.89 per gallon with car wash.
Car wash $8

a. Write an equation describing the cost of g gallons at the regular price.
$$c = 1.29g$$

b. Write an equation describing the cost of g gallons with a car wash.
$$c = .89g + 8$$

c. Graph the two equations from Parts a and b.

c Cost
$c = 8 + .89g$
20
10
$c = 1.29g$
10 20 g
Gallons

d. Use your graph to tell when the cost is the same with or without a car wash.
for 20 gal

e. What equation could be used to answer the question in Part d?
$$1.29g = .89g + 8$$

f. Karen needs 10 gallons of gas. Is it cheaper to get her car washed also?
No

51

LESSON MASTER 5-5 A

Representations Objective J

In 1-3, use the window at the right.

1. Write two inequalities for the window.
$$-6 \le x \le 6, -2 \le y \le 8$$

2. As you move from $x = -4$ to $x = 1$, what happens to the height of the graph?
It increases.

3. What are the coordinates of the point where the graph crosses the y-axis?
(0, 2)

4. What are the coordinates of the highest point on the graph?
(3, 5)

5. Describe a window that would show the highest point in the center of the screen.
Sample: $-3 \le x \le 9$; $0 \le y \le 10$

In 6 and 7, graph $y = x^2 - 4x - 21$ on an automatic grapher, using the given window. Sketch the graph, being sure to show the limits of the window and the axes, if they appear.

6. window: $-5 \le x \le 5$; $-5 \le y \le 5$

7. window: $0 \le x \le 30$; $-10 \le y \le 10$

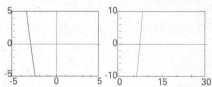

8. a. Use the window $-15 \le x \le 15$, $-10 \le y \le 10$, and graph the two equations $y = 3 - x$ and $y = x - 3$. Sketch the graphs at the right.

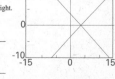

b. Use the graph to find a value of x for which $x - 3 \ne 3 - x$.
Sample: $x = 5$

c. Use the graph to find a value of x for which $x - 3 = 3 - x$.
$$x = 3$$

52

LESSON MASTER 5-6 A

Questions on SPUR Objectives
See pages 343-346 for objectives.

Skills Objective B

1. Write an inequality to find the values of x that make $10x - 12$ greater than $4x + 42$. $10x - 12 > 4x + 42$

In 2–7 solve and check. **Checks are not given.**

2. $-2y - 10 > 3y + 5$

$y < -3$

3. $12y + 3 + 4y \geq 2(7y + 1)$

$y \geq -.5$, or $-\frac{1}{2}$

4. $8y < 10y - 30$

$y > 15$

5. $-4.8m - 3 > 10 - 5.2m$

$m > 32.5$

6. $4(2n - 1) \leq 4(n - 1)$

$n \leq 0$

7. $(20x + 180) - (30x + 50) < 40x - 60$

$x > 3.8$, or $3\frac{4}{5}$

Properties Objective E

9. Show your work as you solve $4x - 8 < 9 - 2x$.
   a. by adding $-4x$ to both sides.   b. by adding $2x$ to both sides.

$4x - 8 + -4x < 9 -$ $4x + 2x - 8 < 9 - 2x + 2x$
$2x + -4x$ $6x - 8 < 9; \; x < \frac{17}{6}$
$-8 < 9 - 6x; \; \frac{17}{6} > x$

   c. Which method is easier? Explain why.
   Sample: Adding $2x$ is easier because the sense of the inequality does not need to be reversed.

Uses Objective F

10. A mail-order club sells CDs for $10.99 each, but charges $10 to join. Sarah pays $13.99 for a CD in a store.
   a. If Sarah buys 20 CDs, is her total cost less in a store or through the club?   **through club**
   b. What is the maximum number of CDs for which the store is less expensive?   **3 CDs**
   c. If the club charges an additional $2 per CD for shipping, what is the maximum number of CDs for which the store is less expensive?   **10 CDs**

LESSON MASTER 5-7 A

Questions on SPUR Objectives
See pages 343-346 for objectives.

Skills Objective D

In 1–8, solve the formula for the given variable.

1. $K = C + 273$ for C

$C = K - 273$

2. $m = 12y$ for y

$y = \frac{m}{12}$

3. $p = 2a + b$ for a

$a = \frac{p - b}{2}$

4. $V = \frac{1}{3}Bh$ for h

$h = \frac{3V}{B}$

5. $p = 2(\ell + w)$ for ℓ

$\ell = \frac{p}{2} - w$

6. $C = \frac{3}{10}S$ for S

$S = \frac{10C}{3}$

7. $C = 180 - A - B$ for A

$A = 180 - B - C$

8. $s = \frac{n}{2}(f + \ell)$ for ℓ

$\ell = \frac{2s}{n} - f$

9. The formula $C = p\left(\frac{\ell w}{9}\right)$ gives the cost C of carpeting a room ℓ feet long and w feet wide, where p = price per square yard of the carpeting. Solve $C = p\left(\frac{\ell w}{9}\right)$ for ℓ. $\ell = \frac{9C}{pw}$

In 10–13, solve the equation for y.

10. $5x + y = 35$

$y = 35 - 5x$

11. $-6 = x - y$

$y = x + 6$

12. $20 = -12x + 4y$

$y = 3x + 5$

13. $3x - 3y = 15$

$y = x - 5$

Properties Objective E

14. Solve the equation $7m + 5 = 3m - 7$ by first adding
   a. $-7m$ to both sides.   b. $-3m$ to both sides.

$m = -3$ $m = -3$

   c. How are your solutions related?
   They are equal.

LESSON MASTER 5-8 A

Questions on SPUR Objectives
See pages 343-346 for objectives.

Skills Objective A

In 1–4, solve the equation.

1. $\frac{5n}{6} + 3 = 10$

$n = \frac{42}{5}$, or 8.4

2. $\frac{7}{8} = \frac{4}{3} - \frac{1}{4}a$

$a = \frac{11}{6}$

3. $4x + .02 = 1.5x + 9$

$x = 3.592$

4. $\frac{2}{3}\left(2x + \frac{1}{2}\right) = \frac{2}{3}x - 8$

$x = -12\frac{1}{2}$, or -12.5

Skills Objective B

In 5–8, solve the inequality.

5. $\frac{-x}{4} + \frac{5}{6} < \frac{4x}{3} + 2$

$x > -\frac{14}{19}$

6. $700y + 200 \geq 1100 - 100y$

$y \geq \frac{9}{8}$

7. $-\frac{n}{5} + 6 > n$

$n < 5$

8. $\frac{1}{10}a + \frac{1}{2}a + \frac{3}{8} \leq 1$

$a < \frac{25}{24}$

Properties Objective E

In 9 and 10, write the equation that results when you multiply through by the given number.

9. In $\frac{4}{9}n + \frac{1}{3} = 5$, multiply both sides by 9. $4n + 3 = 45$

10. In $8x + \frac{3}{5} = \frac{x}{2} - \frac{7}{4}$, multiply both sides by 20. $160x + 12 = 10x - 35$

11. Jenny and Pedro disagree about how to solve $\frac{3}{10}x + 4 = \frac{5}{6}$.
   Jenny says to multiply by 60 and Pedro says to multiply by 30. Which way is better? Why?
   Sample: Pedro's way, because his resulting numbers are smaller

---

▶ **LESSON MASTER 5-8 A** *page 2*

12. Tell what to multiply each side by to make the sentence easier to solve.
   a. $4,000m + 10,000 < 168,000$ $\frac{1}{1,000}$ or $\frac{1}{2,000}$
   b. $.4m + 1 < 16.8$ **10**

13. Fill in the blank with a property or an operation with a given number to explain the step taken to solve $t = a + (n - 1)d$ for n.

$t = a + (n - 1)d$

$t = a + nd - d$ **Distributive** Property

$t - a = nd - d$ **Add -a** to each side.

$t - a + d = nd$ **Add d** to each side.

$\frac{1}{d}(t - a + d) = n$ **Multiply** each side by $\frac{1}{d}$.

Uses Objective F

14. Of the money that an emergency-relief organization spent last year, $\frac{3}{5}$ was for emergency food and $\frac{1}{4}$ was for emergency shelter. The rest, which came to $400,000, was used for expenses.
   a. Write an equation to describe this situation. $\frac{3}{5}x + \frac{1}{4}x + 400,000 = x$
   b. How much did the organization spend last year? $\approx \$2,666,667$
   c. Check your answer to Part **b** by finding the total amount of money used for food and shelters. $\approx \$2,666,667$

15. A baseball team is raising money by selling magazine subscriptions. Donato accounted for $\frac{1}{4}$ of the team's sales and Marty made $\frac{3}{8}$. Together they sold 48 subscriptions. How many did the team sell altogether?   **128 subscriptions**

Name _____

LESSON MASTER 5-9 A

Questions on SPUR Objectives
See pages 343-346 for objectives.

Skills Objective C

1. If $11x = 6$, find the value of $33x + 50$. **68**

2. If $2n = 4.1$, find the value of $12n + 1$. **25.6**

3. If $15x + 3 = 297$, find the value of $15x + 4$. **298**

4. If $5.2y - 16.9 = 85.2$, find the value of $10(5.2y - 16.9)$. **852**

In 6–13, use chunking to simplify the expression.

6. $6(5y + 2) + 4(5y + 2)$

$50y + 20$

7. $-8(x^2 + 3) + 5(x^2 + 3) - 9(x^2 + 3)$

$-12x^3 - 36$

8. $\frac{3}{2x + 5} + \frac{9}{2x + 5}$

$\frac{12}{2x + 5}$

9. $\frac{12y}{x^2 - 11} - \frac{2y}{x^2 - 11}$

$\frac{10y}{x^2 - 11}$

10. $\frac{x + 9}{6} \cdot \frac{15}{x + 9}$

$\frac{5}{2}$

11. $\frac{18}{5(x - 1)} \cdot \frac{2(x - 1)}{11}$

$\frac{36}{55}$

12. $8\sqrt{13} + 9\sqrt{13}$

$17\sqrt{13}$

13. $10\sqrt{2} - \sqrt{2}$

$9\sqrt{2}$

In 14–17, solve the equation.

14. $(y - 1)^2 = 49$

$y = 8$ or $y = -6$

15. $(x + 8)^2 = 1$

$x = -7$ or $x = -9$

16. $(2n + 10)^2 = 144$

$n = 1$ or $n = -11$

17. $(5x)^2 = 900$

$x = 6$ or $x = -6$

18. If $\sqrt{x + 5} = 64$, what is the value

a. of $x + 5$? **4096**

b. of x? **4091**

Name _____

LESSON MASTER 6-1 A

Questions on SPUR Objectives
See pages 412-415 for objectives.

Skills Objective A

In 1–6, fill in the blanks.

1. $\frac{2}{n} = $ **2** $\div$ **n**

2. $\frac{5n}{8} = 5n \cdot$ **$\frac{1}{8}$**

3. $\frac{\frac{3n}{a}}{\frac{5x}{w}} = $ **$\frac{3n}{a}$** $\div$ **$\frac{5x}{w}$**

4. $\frac{5}{n} \div \frac{x + 6}{a} = $ **$\frac{5}{n}$** $\cdot$ **$\frac{a}{x + 6}$**

5. $\frac{1}{n} \div -48 = \frac{1}{n} \cdot$ **$\frac{-1}{48}$**

6. $\frac{x}{\frac{a}{b}} = $ **x** $\cdot$ **$\frac{b}{a}$**

In 7–14, simplify.

7. $\frac{2n}{5} \div \frac{n}{10}$ **4**

8. $\frac{-5}{n} \div 2x$ **$\frac{-5}{2nx}$**

9. $\frac{\frac{2}{5}}{\frac{7}{8}}$ **$\frac{16}{35}$**

10. $\frac{\frac{n}{12}}{-\frac{n}{30}}$ **$\frac{5}{2}$**

11. $\frac{a}{4x} \div \frac{ax}{5}$ **$\frac{5}{4x^2}$**

12. $\frac{\frac{5x}{15}}{x}$ **$\frac{x^2}{3}$**

13. $\frac{\frac{1}{n}}{n}$ **$\frac{1}{n^2}$**

14. $\frac{3\frac{1}{2}}{-\frac{4}{7}}$ **$\frac{49}{8}$**

Name _____

LESSON MASTER 6-2 A

Questions on SPUR Objectives
See pages 412-415 for objectives.

Uses Objective E

1. The world's first steam-powered railroad trip took place in England in 1804. The trip took 4 hours and covered a distance of $9\frac{1}{2}$ miles.

a. What was the train's average speed in miles per hour?

$2\frac{3}{8}$ mph

b. How long did it take the train to travel one mile?

$\frac{8}{19}$ hr

In 2–7, give a rate for each situation. **Samples are given.**

2. The divers dove 300 meters in 45 seconds. **$\frac{60 \text{ m}}{9 \text{ sec}}$**

3. The divers rose 15 m to the surface in 2 min. **$\frac{15 \text{ m}}{2 \text{ min}}$**

4. Today $2\frac{1}{2}$ inches of rain fell in 2 hours. **$\frac{1\frac{1}{4} \text{ in.}}{4 \text{ hr}}$**

5. A 6-oz steak contains about 660 calories. **$110 \frac{\text{calories}}{\text{oz}}$**

6. The Lees' car traveled 450 miles on 17.6 gallons of gasoline. **$\approx 25.6 \frac{\text{mi}}{\text{gal}}$**

7. In 1790, the first U.S. Census reported that the area of the U.S. was 864,746 square miles and the population was 3,929,214. **$\approx 4.5 \frac{\text{people}}{\text{mi}}$**

8. A grocery store sells a 48-oz bottle of apple juice for $1.50 and a 36-oz bottle for $1.19. Find the unit cost (cost per ounce) of the

a. larger bottle. **3.125¢/oz**

b. smaller bottle. **3.306¢/oz**

c. Which is the better buy? **larger bottle**

In 9–11 give the density of each item (weight per volume).

ITEM	WEIGHT	VOLUME	DENSITY
9. egg	62 grams	50 cubic centimeters	**1.24 g/cm³**
10. onion	105 grams	100 cubic centimeters	**1.05 g/cm³**
11. banana	180 grams	190 cubic centimeters	**$\approx$ 0.95 g/cm³**

12. Which is faster, running $3x$ laps in $2m$ minutes or $5x$ laps in $3m$ minutes? Explain your answer.

$5x$ laps in $3m$ minutes; sample: $\frac{3x}{2m} = 1.5 \frac{x\text{laps}}{m\text{min}}$ and $\frac{5x}{3m} = 1.\overline{6} \frac{x\text{laps}}{m\text{min}}$; $1.\overline{6} > 1.5$, so $5x$ laps in $3m$ minutes is faster.

Name _____

LESSON MASTER 6-3 A

Questions on SPUR Objectives
See pages 412-415 for objectives.

Uses Objectives F and H

1. In the 1992 men's national weightlifting championships, Brian Okala, in the 52-kg class, lifted 87.5 kg. Rick Schultz, in the 110-kg class, lifted 162.5 kg. Who lifted more in relation to his body weight?

Okala

2. Maria's special sauce for vegetables is made of 5 parts mayonnaise, 2 parts mustard, and 1 part lemon juice. How much of each ingredient should she use to make 2 cups of the sauce?

$1\frac{1}{4}$ c mayonnaise **$\frac{1}{2}$ c** mustard **$\frac{1}{4}$ c** lemon juice

3. In his major-league career, Babe Ruth had 2,873 hits in 8,399 times at bat. What was his lifetime batting average? (*Batting average* is the ratio of hits to times at bat, expressed as a decimal rounded to the nearest thousandth.)

$\approx$ 0.342

4. According to the census, the 1990 U.S. population was about 248,710,000. California had about 29,760,000 residents and Montana had about 799,000. Find the percent of the U.S. population that lived

a. in California. **$\approx$ 11.97%**

b. in Montana. **$\approx$ 0.32%**

5. A tent originally costing $125.95 is on sale for $107.60. After tax is added, the price is $114.06.

a. What is the percent of discount? **$\approx$ 14.57%**

b. What is the percent of tax? **$\approx$ 6.08%**

6. Companies keep statistics on different TV shows to judge which are the most popular and to determine advertising fees. A show's *rating* is the percent of households with TVs that watch the show. A show's *share* is the percent of households with the TV *on* that watch the show. Suppose a city has 2,000,000 households with TV and at 10 P.M. 830,000 are watching TV. Of those 90,000 are watching the Channel 3 News.

a. Give the rating. **4.5%**

b. Give the share. **$\approx$ 10.8%**

c. A very popular show could have a rating of 25%. How many people in this city can be expected to watch such a show?

500,000 people

Name _____

LESSON MASTER 6-4 A

Questions on SPUR Objectives
See pages 412-415 for objectives.

Uses Objective G

1. A survey asked people to name their favorite sport. Give the relative frequency as a fraction of people who like baseball best if

a. 385 people were polled and 315 did *not* pick baseball.

$$\frac{2}{11} \approx 18.2\%$$

b. 209 people were polled and 150 did *not* pick baseball.

$$\frac{59}{209} \approx 28.2\%$$

c. 950 people were polled and x did *not* pick baseball.

$$\frac{950 - x}{950}$$

d. p people were polled and n did *not* pick baseball.

$$\frac{p - n}{p}$$

2. As of May, 1992, of about 92,000,000 U.S. households that had TVs, there were close to 56,000,000 that had cable TV. Estimate the relative frequency of households with TVs that

a. also had cable. $\frac{14}{23} \approx$ **60.9%**

b. did not have cable. $\frac{9}{23} \approx$ **39.1%**

3. A charity sold 418 raffle tickets. One ticket will be drawn and the ticket-holder will receive a new bicycle. Hojung bought 5 tickets. Let the event E = Hojung wins and S = set of all outcomes. Find

a. $N(E)$, **5**

b. $N(S)$, **418**

c. $P(E)$, $\frac{5}{418} \approx$ **1%**

d. P(Hojung does not win). $\frac{413}{418} \approx$ **99%**

In 4–6 a card is drawn from a regular deck. Find

4. P(queen). $\frac{1}{13} \approx$ **7.7%**

5. P(jack, queen, or king). $\frac{3}{13} \approx$ **23.1%**

6. P(queen of hearts). $\frac{1}{52} \approx$ **1.9%**

7. Lucy fills a pot with a mixture of 1200 black beans and 300 white beans, all the same size. When she grabs a handful of 15 beans, she finds that 10 are black.

a. What is the probability of choosing a white bean? $\frac{1}{5} =$ **20%**

b. What is Lucy's relative frequency of choosing a white bean? $\frac{1}{3} \approx$ **33.3%**

c. Why do the answers to Parts **a** and **b** do not have to be the same?

Sample: Relative frequency is based on an experiment; probability is deduced from an assumption.

61

Name _____

LESSON MASTER 6-5 A

Questions on SPUR Objectives
See pages 412-415 for objectives.

Skills Objective B

1. 15 out of 180 is what percent?

$$8\frac{1}{3}\%$$

2. 4.8 is what percent of 6.2?

$$\approx 77.4\%$$

3. What is 2% of 497?

$$9.94$$

4. What is 6.8% of 500?

$$34$$

5. What is 28% of $36,000?

$$\$10,080$$

6. 85% of what number is 119?

$$140$$

7. 40% of a number is 73. What is the number?

$$182.5$$

8. 5% of a number is 635. What is the number?

$$12,700$$

Uses Objective H

9. School health records show that 70% of the children have been immunized against polio. If the school has 350 children, how many have had a polio immunization?

245 children

10. A headline reads: ACME, INC., LAYS OFF 15% OF WORK FORCE 2500 People to Lose Jobs

How many workers did Acme employ before the layoff?

$$\approx 16,667 \text{ workers}$$

11. In 1990, about 79.3% of the U.S. population lived in metropolitan areas. The U.S. population was about 249 million people. How many lived

a. in metropolitan areas?

$$\approx 197,460,000 \text{ people}$$

b. outside metropolitan areas?

$$\approx 51,540,000 \text{ people}$$

12. After 6% sales tax was added, a T-shirt cost $9.53. Find the cost of the T-shirt without tax.

$$\$8.99$$

13. A sweater is on sale for 30% off. The sale price is $22.40. What is the regular price?

$$\$32$$

14. A marine biologist found that there are about 20% more of a certain type of fish in the area in summer than in winter. She estimated that in the summer there are 1500 of these fish in the bay. How many are there in winter?

$$\approx 1250 \text{ fish}$$

62

Name _____

LESSON MASTER 6-6 A

Questions on SPUR Objectives
See pages 412-415 for objectives.

Representations Objective J

1. In a 40-ft-by-100-ft field is a dog on a 12-foot chain. If some children hit a softball into the field, what is the probability that the ball will land within reach of the dog?

$$\frac{9\pi}{250} \approx 11.3\%$$

40 ft.

100 ft.

2. This target is made of circles with radii of 10, 15, and 20 inches.

a. Find the area of each circle.

100π, 225π, 400π in.²

b. Find the area of the shaded region.

125π in.²

c. If a dart is thrown at random, what is the probability that it will land in the shaded ring?

$$\frac{5}{16} \approx 6.25\%$$

d. What is the probability that it will land in the outermost ring?

$$\frac{7}{16} \approx 43.8\%$$

3. |———————A B——————————|
   2 miles   ¼ mile   3¼ miles

Ben plans to march in a parade in Washington, D.C., which will go past a reviewing stand where the President will sit to watch. The parade route is shown. The portion between A and B is in view of the reviewing stand. If Ben trips at a random point along the route, what is the probability that the President might see him trip?

$$\frac{1}{22} \approx 4.5\%$$

For 4 and 5, give the probability that the spinner will land in region A.

4.

$$\frac{1}{6} \approx 16.7\%$$

5.

$$\frac{1}{4} \approx 25\%$$

63

Name _____

LESSON MASTER 6-7 A

Questions on SPUR Objectives
See pages 412-415 for objectives.

Uses Objective H

In 1–3, Mayuko enlarged a picture (A) on a photocopy machine by a factor of 130%. She decided the result (B) wasn't quite large enough so she enlarged it again by a factor of 110% (C).

A   B   C

Find the height of the other two pictures if the height of

1. picture A is 10 in.

B **13 in.**
C **14.3 in.**

2. picture B is 10 in.

A $\approx$ **7.7 in.**
C **11 in.**

3. picture C is 24 in.

A $\approx$ **16.8 in.**
B $\approx$ **21.8 in.**

Representations Objective K

4. a. Graph quadrilateral $ABCD$ if $A = (4, -2)$, $B = (2, 0)$, $C = (5, 4)$ and $D = (4, 0)$.

b. Graph the image $A'B'C'D'$ under a size change of magnitude 2.

c. Graph $A''B''C''D''$, the image of $ABCD$, under a size change of magnitude $\frac{1}{2}$.

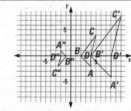

5. A figure undergoes a size change under the rule that the image of (x, y) is $(5x, 5y)$. How does this affect the figure's size?

Image segments are 5 times as long as corresponding preimage segments.

In 6–8, the magnitude of a size change is given. Tell if it is an *expansion*, a *contraction*, or *neither*.

6. $k = \frac{2}{3}$

contraction

7. $k = -10$

expansion

8. $k = 1$

neither

64

158

LESSON MASTER 6-8 A

Questions on SPUR Objectives
See pages 412-415 for objectives.

Skills Objective C

In 1-6, use the Means-Extremes Property to solve.

1. $\frac{7}{8} = \frac{x}{4}$
$x = \frac{7}{2}$, or 3.5

2. $\frac{5a}{3} = \frac{15}{2}$
$a = \frac{9}{2}$, or 4.5

3. $\frac{18}{w+8} = \frac{2}{3}$
$w = 19$

4. $\frac{2x+1}{3} = \frac{5x-5}{6}$
$x = 7$

5. $\frac{v+5}{v+7} = -8$
$v = -\frac{61}{9}$, or -6.8

6. $\frac{2}{w} = \frac{w}{18}$
$w = 6$ or $w = -6$

In 7 and 8, a. give the exact solutions, and
b. give the solutions rounded to the nearest hundredth.

7. $\frac{x}{3} = \frac{1}{x}$
a. $x = \sqrt{3}$ or $-\sqrt{3}$
b. $x = 1.73$ or -1.73

8. $\frac{5}{2y} = \frac{y}{6}$
a. $y = \sqrt{15}$ or $-\sqrt{15}$
b. $x = 3.87$ or -3.87

Properties Objective D

9. Explain how you can use the Means-Extremes Property to determine if the fractions $\frac{3}{5}$ and $\frac{7.5}{12.5}$ are equal.
Sample: Find the product of means (5·7.5) and extremes (3·12.5). If the products are equal, the fractions are equal.

Uses Objective I

10. In 1990, 39.5 million foreigners visited the U.S. Of these, 17.3 million were from Canada. If the total number of visitors increases to 50 million in the year 2000, how many can be expected to be from Canada?
≈ 22.1 million

11. Carlo figures that when he is driving at highway speed his car's engine turns at a rate of 3000 revolutions per minute. He has also found that when the engine turns 7 times, the wheels turn 2 times. If Carlo drives for 1 hour,
a. how many times does the engine turn?
180,000 times
b. how many times does a wheel turn?
≈ 51,400 times

12. On the 10 o'clock news, the sportscaster can cover 10 sports stories in 3 minutes 45 seconds. If his time slot is increased to 5 minutes, how many stories can he cover?
≈ 13 stories

65

LESSON MASTER 6-9 A

Questions on SPUR Objectives
See pages 412-415 for objectives.

Representations Objective L

1. Two common sizes for photographs are 5 in. by 7 in. and 8 in. by 10 in.
a. What is the ratio of the widths of the pictures? $\frac{5}{8}$
b. What is the ratio of the lengths of the pictures? $\frac{7}{10}$
c. Are the pictures similar? Explain why or why not.
no; sample: Lengths of corresponding sides are not proportional.

2. Triangle CAT is similar to triangle DOG.
a. Calculate $\frac{CT}{DG}$.
$\frac{5}{9}$, or 0.5̄
b. Find two ratios of sides equal to $\frac{CT}{DG}$.
$\frac{CA}{DO}$ $\frac{AT}{OG}$
c. What side of $\triangle DOG$ corresponds to $\overline{CA}$ in $\triangle CAT$?
$\overline{DO}$
d. Write a proportion to find the length of $\overline{DO}$.
$\frac{DO}{8} = \frac{9}{5}$

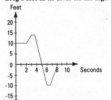

In 3-5, the two trapezoids are similar. Find the length of

3. $\overline{AB}$. $31\frac{1}{4}$, or 31.25

4. $\overline{BC}$. 50

5. $\overline{DC}$. $70\frac{5}{16}$, or 70.3125

6. These triangles are similar.
a. Find x and $x + 8$.
5 and 13
b. Find the length of the third side of each triangle. (Hint: Do not use a proportion.)
12 and 24
c. Give two possible ratios of similitude.
$\frac{1}{2}$, 2

66

LESSON MASTER 7-1 A

Questions on SPUR Objectives
See pages 480-483 for objectives.

Uses Objective E

In 1-5, use the chart below. It shows the number to the nearest million of U.S. households with cable TV every five years from 1970 to 1990.

Year	1970	1975	1980	1985	1990
Households	4 million	9 million	15 million	36 million	55 million

1. Graph the information on the grid at the left. Connect the points.

2. Which segment is steeper, the one connecting (1975, 9 million) to (1980, 15 million) or the one connecting (1980, 15 million) to (1985, 36 million)?
from (1980, 15) to (1985, 36)

3. What was the rate of change of number of households with cable from 1970 to 1975?
1 million households/year

4. What was the rate of change of the number of households with cable from 1985 to 1990?
3.8 million households/year

5. For the years shown, was the rate of change ever negative?
no

In 6 and 7, use the table at the right. It shows the prices a vacation resort charges for stays of the given durations.

Days	Cost
3	$289
4	$359
7	$449

6. a. What is the rate of change from a 4-day vacation to a 7-day vacation?
$30/day
b. What is the unit of the rate of change?
dollars per day

7. Is the rate of change from 3 to 4 days the same as the rate of change from 4 days to 7 days?
no

67 ▶

In 8-12, use the graph below. It shows the height of Greg's feet as he dives off the high board.

8. How many seconds pass before Greg's feet leave the board?
2 seconds

9. How long is he in the air?
3 seconds

10. About how high does he jump?
4 ft from board;
14 ft from water

11. What is happening between 5 and 6 seconds?
He is entering the water.

12. How high is the diving board?
10 feet

In 13-14, use this spreadsheet. It shows the average number of pounds of plastic each person in the U.S. discards each year, projected through the year 2000.

	A	B	C
1	YEAR	POUNDS	RATE OF CHANGE IN POUNDS/YEAR DURING PREVIOUS DECADE
2	1960	3.7	
3	1970	29.2	2.55
4	1980	69.4	4.02
5	1990	116.8	4.74
6	2000	157.0	4.02

13. What formula could be in cell C5?
=(B5−B4)/10

14. Complete the spreadsheet.

68

159

Name

LESSON MASTER 7-2 A

Skills Objective A

In 1 and 2, calculate the slope of the line through the two points.

1. (3, 20) and (7, 36) __4__

2. (-6, 5) and (10, 9) $\frac{1}{4}$

In 3 and 4, find the slope of the line.

3. $-\frac{5}{2}$

4. 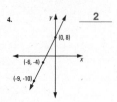 2

(0, 8)
(3, -3)
(5, -8)
(-6, -4)
(-9, -10)

5. The points (1, 8) and (m, 14) are on a line with slope 3. Find the value of m. __m = 3__

Properties Objective D

6. If a line passes through the points (a, b) and (j, k), what is its slope? $\frac{k-b}{j-a}(j \ne a)$

7. Explain how to tell if the slope of a line is positive, negative, or zero by looking at its graph.

Sample: up from left to right–positive; down from left to right–negative; horizontal–zero

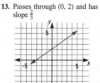

For 8–10, use the graph at the left.

8. Name two points on a line with positive slope. **B, C**

9. Name two points on a line with zero slope. **B, D**

10. The slope determined by points A and D seems equal to the slope determined by which two points?

C and D

69

Name

LESSON MASTER 7-3 A

Properties Objective D

1. Fill in the blanks. If the slope of a line is -4, then as you go __1__ unit(s) to the right you go __4__ unit(s) **down**

2. a. Give an example of coordinates of two points that lie on the same horizontal line. **Sample: (8, 3), (5, 3)**

   b. Use the points from Part a to explain why the slope of a horizontal line is zero.
   Slope is $\frac{3-3}{8-5} = \frac{0}{3} = 0.$

3. a. Give an example of coordinates of two points that lie on the same vertical line. **Sample: (2, 6), (2, 3)**

   b. Use the points from Part a to explain why the slope of a vertical line is undefined.
   Slope is $\frac{6-3}{2-2} = \frac{3}{0},$ **which is undefined.**

In 4–7, tell which line has the given slope.

4. 0 **p**

5. negative **m**

6. positive **l**

7. undefined **n**

In 8–10, consider the line which goes through the point (10, -2) and has the indicated slope. Name another point with integer coordinates that lies on the line. **Samples are given.**

8. 3 **(11, 1)**

9. -1 **(11, -3)**

10. $\frac{1}{2}$ **(12, -1)**

Uses Objective E

11. In order for the Wassermans to install their new washing machine, they had to move the old machine out of their basement. To do this, they built a small ramp by laying a piece of plywood over the 5 steps leading to the outside. If the rise (the vertical part) of each step was 6 inches and the run (the horizontal part) of each step was 9 inches, what was the slope of the ramp? $\frac{2}{3}$

70

Name

▶ **LESSON MASTER 7-3 A** *page 2*

Representations Objective H

In 12 and 13, graph the line described.

12. Passes through (-1, 4) and has slope -2.

13. Passes through (0, 2) and has slope $\frac{6}{3}$.

14. **Cost**

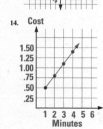

A long-distance call from Midland to Valleyhill costs $.50 for the first minute, plus $.30 for each additional minute.

Sample points are given.

a. Give the coordinates of four points showing (duration of call, cost).
(1, .50) (2, .80)
(3, 1.10) (4, 1.40)

b. Draw a graph showing how the cost changes as the minutes increase.

15. Two minutes after diving from the surface of the ocean, a submarine was 100 m below the surface. Then it descended 15 m every minute.

Sample points are given.

a. Write the coordinates of four points showing (minutes, position of submarine).
(2, -100) (3, -115)
(4, -130) (5, -145)

b. Draw a graph showing how the sub's position changed over time.

71

Name

LESSON MASTER 7-4 A

Vocabulary

1. Write the *slope-intercept form* of the equation of a line. $y = mx + b$

In 2–5, use the graph below.

2. What is the *y-intercept* of line p? **1**

3. What is the *slope* of line p? **2**

4. What is the *y-intercept* of line n? **-1**

5. What is the *slope* of line n? **0**

Skills Objective B

In 6 and 7, a line is described. Write its equation in slope-intercept form.

6. slope $\frac{2}{3}$, y-intercept 4
$y = \frac{2}{3}x + 4$

7. slope -5, y-intercept 0
$y = -5x$

In 8 and 9, a line is graphed. a. Give the slope of the line. b. Give the y-intercept. c. Write an equation for the line.

8.

9.

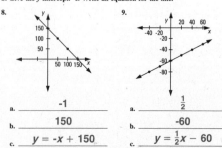

a. **-1**

a. $\frac{1}{2}$

b. **150**

b. **-60**

c. $y = -x + 150$

c. $y = \frac{1}{2}x - 60$

72

160

Name _____

► **LESSON MASTER 7-4 A** *page 2*

Skills Objective C

In 10 and 11, an equation of a line is given.
a. Change the equation to slope-intercept form.
b. Give the slope.   c. Give the y-intercept.

10. $4x + 5y = 15$ a. $y = -\frac{4}{5}x + 3$ b. $-\frac{4}{5}$ c. 3

11. $x - y = -3$ a. $y = x + 3$ b. 1 c. 3

Uses Objective F

12. The basic fee for repairing a piece of machinery is $75 plus $20 for each hour of labor. If this were described by a graph, give the

   a. y-intercept. 75 b. slope. 20

13. The price of a cheese pizza is $4.50 with a charge of $0.50 for each additional topping. If this situation were graphed with x = number of toppings and y = total price, give the

   a. y-intercept. 4.5 b. slope. 0.5

   c. equation. $y = 0.5x + 4.5$

Representations Objective H

In 14 and 15, graph the line.

14. slope -3, y-intercept 5

15. $-2x + y = 1$

73

Name _____

Questions on SPUR Objectives
See pages 480-483 for objectives.

Skills Objective B

In 1–4, a point and slope are given. Write an equation for the line with that slope that passes through the point.

1. slope 5, point (2, -1) $y = 5x - 11$

2. slope -3, point (-6, 0) $y = -3x - 18$

3. slope $\frac{1}{4}$, point (-1, -8) $y = \frac{1}{4}x - \frac{31}{4}$

4. slope $-\frac{2}{5}$, point (6, 4) $y = -\frac{2}{5}x + \frac{32}{5}$

5.

a. Write an equation for the line graphed at the left. $y = -2x + 20$

b. What are the coordinates of point T? $(8, 4)$

c. Show that the coordinates of point T satisfy your equation from Part a.
   $4 = -2(8) + 20?$ $4 = 4$

d. At what point will the line cross the y-axis? $(0, 20)$

Uses Objective F

In 6 and 7, a situation is given. a. Give a possible point (x, y).
b. Write an equation for a line which relates x and y. c. Find the slope of the line. d. Answer the question.

6. A hardware store sells extension ladders. A 16-ft ladder costs $50 and the price increases $7.50 for each additional foot of ladder length. Let x = ladder length and y = price. What is the cost of a 28-ft ladder?

   a. $(16, 50)$ b. $y = 7.5x - 70$

   c. 7.5 d. $\$140$

7. Felicita's Fashions is having a sale on dresses. By the 8th day of the sale, there were 130 dresses left. The store sells about 25 dresses each day. Let x = the number of days since the sale started and y = the number of dresses left. How many days will it take to sell all the dresses?

   a. $(8, 30)$ b. $y = -25x + 330$

   c. -25 d. 14 days

74

Name _____

Questions on SPUR Objectives
See pages 480-483 for objectives.

Skills Objective B

In 1–4, write the equation in slope-intercept form of the line containing the two points.

1. (1, 5) and (3, 14) $y = \frac{9}{2}x + \frac{1}{2}$

2. (-2, -4) and (3, 16) $y = 4x + 4$

3. (6, 0) and (11, -5) $y = -x + 6$

4. (12, 18) and (3, 12) $y = \frac{2}{3}x + 10$

5. a. Give an equation for the line that contains (3, 2) and (5, -2).
   $y = -2x + 8$

   b. Check your answer by graphing the line on the grid at the right.

Uses Objective F

In 6 and 7, a situation is described. a. Give two ordered pairs for the situation. b. Write an equation for the line through the two points. c. Answer the question.

6. A loop of string is formed into a rectangle. If the width of the rectangle is 12 inches, the height is 6 inches. If the width is 10 inches, the height is 8 inches. Let w = width and h = height. If the width is 15 inches, what is the height?

   a. $(12, 16), (10, 8)$ b. $h = -w + 18$

   c. 3 inches

7. When the Gonzalez family's new kitten was 6 weeks old it weighed 8 ounces. When it was 10 weeks old it weighed 10 ounces. Let x = the age of the kitten and y = the weight of the kitten. If the kitten's weight gain had been linear, how much did it weigh at birth?

   a. $(6, 8), (10, 10)$ b. $y = \frac{1}{2}x + 5$

   c. 5 ounces

75

Name _____

Questions on SPUR Objectives
See pages 480-483 for objectives.

Uses Objective G

1. a. On the first grid make a scatterplot that is approximately linear.

   b. On the second grid make a scatterplot that is *not* approximately linear.

Linear   Not Linear

2. The table below was developed by a French veterinarian, Dr. A. LeBeau. It gives the age of a cat or dog and its corresponding age in human years.

Cat/Dog Age (years)	0.5	1	2	4	6	8	10	14	18	21
Human Age (years)	10	15	24	32	40	48	56	72	91	106

   a. Carefully draw a scatterplot of points (animal age, human age).

   b. Fit a line to the data by eye and draw it with a ruler.

   c. Give the coordinates of two points that lie on the line you drew.
   $(8, 48), (14, 76)$

   d. Use your two points to find an equation for your line.
   $y = \frac{14}{3}x + \frac{32}{3}$

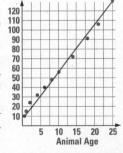

Human Age

Animal Age

   e. According to your equation, what happens to the corresponding human age as the cat or dog ages one year?

   Sample: Human age increases by $\approx 4\frac{2}{3}$ yr.

   f. Use your equation to find the approximate human age equivalent to that of a 15-year-old dog. ≈ 81 yr

   Sample answers are given.

76

161

Lesson Master 7-8

LESSON MASTER 7-8 A

Skills Objective C

In 1 and 2, tell if the equation is in standard form.

1. $y = 3x - 5$ **no**

2. $4x + 2y = 18$ **yes**

In 3–6, an equation is given. a. Rewrite the equation in standard form with integer coefficients. b. Give the values of A, B, and C.

3. $y = -4x - 6$ a. $4x + y = -6$ b. $4, 1, -6$

4. $y = \frac{2}{3}x + 7$ a. $2x - 3y = -21$ b. $2, -3, -21$

5. $y = -\frac{1}{5}x + \frac{1}{3}$ a. $3x + 15y = 5$ b. $3, 15, 5$

6. $y - x = 16$ a. $x - y = -16$ b. $1, -1, -16$

Uses Objective F

7. In a basketball-shooting game you get points in two ways: 10 points if you hit the rim and 50 points if you get a basket. Marcos hit the rim x times and got y baskets. His final score was 200.

   a. Write an equation in standard form that describes the relationship between x and y. $10x + 50y = 200$

   b. Give three solutions to your equation in Part a. Samples: (5, 3), (10, 2), (15, 1)

Representations Objective H

In 8 and 9, an equation is given. a. Find the x- and y-intercepts. b. Use the intercepts to graph the line.

8. $4x + 2y = 12$

   a. $(3, 0), (0, 6)$

   b.

9. $10x - 4y = 20$

   a. $(2, 0), (0, -5)$

   b.

77

Lesson Master 7-9

LESSON MASTER 7-9 A

Representations Objective I

In 1 and 2, write an inequality that describes the graph.

1.

   $y > -2$

2.

   $y \le .6x + 3$

In 3 and 4, tell if a. the shading should be above or below the boundary line, and b. the boundary line should be solid or dashed.

3. $y \le 9x + 3$ a. **below** b. **solid**

4. $y > x - 6$ a. **above** b. **dashed**

In 5 and 6, graph on the number line and the grid.

5. $x > 4$

   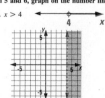

6. $y \le 8$

In 7 and 8, graph all points that satisfy the inequality.

7. $y > 3x - 4$

8. $x - 2y > 6$

78

Lesson Master 8-1

LESSON MASTER 8-1 A

Vocabulary

In 1 and 2, an expression is given. a. Write the expression using exponents. b. Identify the *base(s)*. c. Identify the *exponent(s)*. d. Identify the *coefficient*.

1. $25 \cdot x \cdot x \cdot x$

   a. $25x^3$ b. x c. 3 d. 25

2. $6 \cdot a \cdot a \cdot a \cdot a \cdot a \cdot b \cdot b$

   a. $6a^5b^3$ b. a, b c. $5, 3$ d. 6

Skills Objective A

In 3–5, evaluate. Give answers to the nearest ten-thousandth.

3. 4^3 64

4. 1.35^5 4.48

5. $40(1 + .06)^{10}$ 71.63

Uses Objective F

6. Suppose $2500 is invested at 5.6% annual yield for 15 years.

   a. Write an expression for the total amount at the end of this time. $2500(1 + 0.056)^{15}$

   b. Write a calculator key sequence for your expression. $2500 \boxed{\times} 1.056 \boxed{y^x} 15 \boxed{=}$

7. A bank uses this spreadsheet to show the amount in a savings account earning 7% interest. The principal invested is $600. What formula could be entered in cell

	A	B	C
1	YEAR	BALANCE	ANNUAL INTEREST
2	0	600.00	
3	1	642.00	42.00
4	2	686.94	44.94
5	3	735.03	48.09
6	4	786.48	51.45

   a. B6? $= B5 * 1.07$

   b. C6? $= B6 - B5$

   c. Complete line 6.

   d. What trend do you notice in the annual-interest column? Sample: Amounts of interest increase.

8. Most credit-cards plans charge interest if the monthly bill is not paid. Suppose an $850 bill is not paid for 3 years. If the annual interest rate is 16%, how much is owed? $1326.76

79

Lesson Master 8-2

LESSON MASTER 8-2 A

Skills Objective A

In 1–7, evaluate the expression.

1. 5^0 1

2. $8^0 \cdot 8^2$ 64

3. $5^6 \cdot 5^0$ $15,625$

4. $(a + 15)^0$ when $a = 6$ 1

5. $\left(\frac{3}{8}\right)^2 + \left(\frac{7}{8}\right)^0$ $\frac{73}{64}$

6. $3 \cdot 10^2 + 4 \cdot 10^1 + 9 \cdot 10^0$ 349

7. $400 \cdot 3^n$ when $n = 0$ 400

Properties Objective E

8. Describe a situation that can be modeled with the expression $100 \cdot 2^0$.

   Sample: A colony of 100 organisms doubles its population every 15 minutes.

9. A colony of bacteria doubles every 6 hours. How many times will it double in

   a. 24 hours? **4 times**

   b. 5 days? **20 times**

   c. 2 weeks? **56 times**

Uses Objective G

10. An orange grower introduced a new type of ladybug to his orchards to control pests. He began with 500 ladybugs and feels that the number will naturally increase 5% each month. Based on this information, answer the following questions: In Parts b and c, round values down to the preceding integer.

    a. By how much is the number of ladybugs multiplied each month? 1.05

    b. How many ladybugs will there be after 6 months? ≈ 670 ladybugs

    c. How many ladybugs will there be after 2 years? $\approx 1{,}612$ ladybugs

80 ▶

▶ **LESSON MASTER 8-2 A** *page 2*

11. Anya has started a new job paying $8 per hour. Assuming that her work is excellent, she will get a 5% raise every 4 months.

   a. After 3 years, how many raises will she have gotten?   **9 raises**

   b. What will her pay rate be after 3 years?   **$12.41/hour**

   c. If her employer continues to give her raises in this way, what will her pay rate be after she has been working for 10 years?   **$34.58/hour**

12. Jeff wanted to enlarge a drawing on a copy machine. He first enlarged the original by 30%. He then took the copy he just made and fed it through the copy machine, enlarging it by 30%. He did this 3 more times, each time taking the previous copy and enlarging it by 30%. If the original drawing had been 2 inches by 3 inches, did the final copy fit on a sheet of paper $8\frac{1}{2}$ inches by 11 inches? Explain your answer.

No; sample: The dimensions of the final copy will be ≈7.4 in. by ≈11.1 in., which is too large.

Representations Objective I

13. The president of Acme Industries predicts that the sales of a new product will grow by 35% every year for the next 5 years. This year sales were $40,000.

   a. Make a table of values showing the sales 0, 1, 2, 3, 4, and 5 years from now.

YEARS	SALES
0	$40,000
1	$54,000
2	$72,900
3	$98,415
4	$132,860
5	$179,361

   b. Graph the sales for the first six years.

Sales ($1000s) vs Years

LESSON MASTER   **8-3 A**   **Questions on SPUR Objectives** See pages 543-545 for objectives.

Uses Objective G
Representations Objective I

1. A biologist is studying the effect of a new medicine on the production of antibodies. The antibodies may grow either at a constant rate or exponentially. The biologist studies two cases beginning with 100 antibodies. Case 1: There are 30 more each day. Case 2: There are 20% more each day. Let x = the number of days the antibodies have been growing.

Day	Increase By 30	Increase By 20%
1	130	120
2	160	144
3	190	172
4	220	207
5	250	248
6	280	298
7	310	358
8	340	429
9	370	515
10	400	619

   a. Write an expression for Case 1.   **100 + 3x**

   b. Write an expression for Case 2.   **100(1.2)^x**

   c. Complete the table at the right. Round values down to the preceding integer.

   d. Which case yields more antibodies after 4 days?   **Case 1**

   e. Which case yields more antibodies after 10 days?   **Case 2**

   f. How many antibodies will there be after 100 days in each case?

   Case 1   **3100 antibodies**

   Case 2   **≈8.28(10)^9**

   g. Graph the information in the table on the grid at the right.

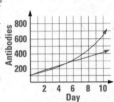

Antibodies vs Day

In 2–5, tell which is being described:
(a) *constant increase* or
(b) *exponential growth.*

2.

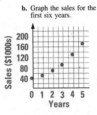

Mosquitos vs Years   **(b)**

3. Each day the water level rose $\frac{1}{2}$ inch.   **(a)**

4. $2000 + 30x$ **(a)**

5. $450 \cdot 1.8^x$ **(b)**

LESSON MASTER   **8-4 A**   **Questions on SPUR Objectives** See pages 543-545 for objectives.

Uses Objective G

1. Investors in the Get-Rich-Quick Investment company lose about 15% of the value of their money each year.

   a. Fill in the table to show the value of a $2,000 investment for each of the first seven years.

YEAR	VALUE
0	$2,000
1	$1,700
2	$1,445
3	$1,228.25
4	$1,044.01
5	$887.41
6	$754.30

   b. How much was lost the first year?   **$300**

   c. How much was lost from the fifth to the sixth year?   **$133.11**

   d. Write an expression for the value of the investment in year x.   **2000(0.85)^x**

   e. Use trial and error to find the first year in which the value is less than $100.   **year 19**

2. Amalgamated Industries receives hundreds of applications for each job opening it has. Their selection process is to review the applications and discard 50% of them. Then this is repeated until only one applicant is left. Let n = the number of times that half the applications are discarded.

   a. Write an expression of the form $b \cdot g^n$ to describe the number of people left after the applications have been reviewed n times.   **b(0.5)^n**

   b. If 512 people apply for a job, how many are left when $n = 4$?   **32 people**

   c. If 512 people apply, what is the value of n when one person is left?   **9**

3. In 1993, the national debt was estimated at 4.4 trillion dollars. Suppose this were cut 10% each year. Let x be the number of years since 1993.

   a. Write an equation to describe this situation.   **d = 4.4·10^{12}(0.9)^x**

   b. What would the deficit be after 20 years?   **≈5.35·10^{11} dollars**

▶ **LESSON MASTER 8-4 A** *page 2*

In 4–7, *multiple choice.* Tell if the situation described is:
   (a) exponential growth.   (b) exponential decay.
   (c) constant increase.   (d) constant decrease.

4. Every year there are 5% fewer patients with the disease.   **b**

5. With better techniques, farmers are able to increase their output 3% each year.   **a**

6. Each year there are 30 fewer students in the school.   **d**

7. Every time Joan took the test her score went up 4 points.   **c**

Representations Objective I

In 8–11, *multiple choice.* Match the graph to the equation.

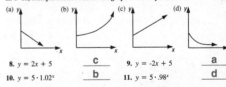

(a)   (b)   (c)   (d)

8. $y = 2x + 5$ **c**

9. $y = -2x + 5$ **a**

10. $y = 5 \cdot 1.02^x$ **b**

11. $y = 5 \cdot .98^x$ **d**

12. At Betty's Bargain Shop, the original price of a designer dress was $200. The price was marked down 30% for each week the dress is not sold. Let x = number of weeks the dress is not sold and y = price of the dress.

   a. Write an equation relating x and y.   **y = 200(0.7)^x**

   b. On the grid at the right, graph the price of the dress from zero to 10 weeks.

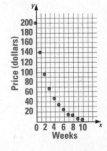

Price (dollars) vs Weeks

Lesson Master 8-5 A

LESSON MASTER 8-5 A

Questions on SPUR Objectives
See pages 543-545 for objectives.

Uses Objective B

In 1–12, simplify the expression.

1. $n^2 \cdot n^6$ n^8 2. $y^8 \cdot y$ y^9

3. $(x^6)^2$ x^{12} 4. $(5^2)^3$ 5^6, or 15,625

5. $(k^0)^2$ 1 6. $x^2 \cdot x^4 \cdot x$ x^7

7. $a^2 \cdot x^3 \cdot a^7$ $a^9 x^3$ 8. $n(n^5)^4$ n^{21}

9. $6^2 \cdot 6^2$ 6^4, or 1296   10. $2x^3 \cdot 8x^4$ $16x^7$

11. $(n \cdot n^4)^3$ n^{15} 12. $x^2(x + x^6)$ $x^3 + x^8$

Properties Objective E

13. Show how to simplify $(n^2)^4$
   a. by treating n^2 as a chunk.
$$(n^2)^4 = n^2 \cdot n^2 \cdot n^2 \cdot n^2 = n^8$$
   b. by using the Power of a Power Property.
$$(n^2)^4 = n^{2 \cdot 4} = n^8$$

14. Show how to simplify $a^5 \cdot a$
   a. by using repeated multiplication.
$$a^5 \cdot a = (a \cdot a \cdot a \cdot a \cdot a) \cdot a = a^6$$
   b. by using the Product of Powers Property.
$$a^5 \cdot a = a^5 \cdot a^1 = a^{5+1} = a^6$$

15. Write a multiplication expression that uses the Product of Powers Property and the value of which is x^{10}.
Samples are given. $x^4 \cdot x^6$

16. Write an expression that uses the Power of a Power Property and the value of which is y^{24}.
$(y^3)^8$

85

Lesson Master 8-6 A

LESSON MASTER 8-6 A

Questions on SPUR Objectives
See pages 543-545 for objectives.

Skills Objective A

In 1–6, evaluate. Give the answer as a simple fraction.

1. 4^{-1} $\frac{1}{4}$ 2. 7^{-2} $\frac{1}{49}$ 3. $\left(\frac{1}{3}\right)^{-1}$ 3

4. 11^{-3} $\frac{1}{1131}$ 5. $5 \cdot 3^{-2}$ $\frac{5}{9}$ 6. $19^4 \cdot 19^{-4}$ 1

Skills Objective B

In 7–10, simplify the expression.

7. $a^{-5} \cdot a^6$ a 8. $n^{-10} \cdot n^3$ n^{-7}, or $\frac{1}{n^7}$

9. $a^3 n^{-6} \cdot a^{-3} n^4$ n^{-2}, or $\frac{1}{n^2}$ 10. $x \cdot x^{-5}$ x^{-4}, or $\frac{1}{x^4}$

11. Give examples of three different pairs of values of a and b such that $x^a \cdot x^b = x^2$.   5, -3   4, -2   1, 1

Properties Objective E

12. How is a^{-n} related to a^n?
Sample: a^{-n} is the reciprocal of a^n.

13. Simplify $n^{-5} \cdot n^5$ by first applying
   a. the Negative Exponent Property.
$$n^{-5} \cdot n^5 = \frac{1}{n^5} \cdot n^5 = \frac{n^5}{n^5} = 1$$
   b. the Product of Powers Property.
$$n^{-5} \cdot n^5 = n^{-5+5} = n^0 = 1$$

Uses Objective G

14. A scientist is studying insects whose population doubles every 5 days. There are 4800 insects today. How many were there 30 days ago?
75 insects

15. Adria has $4,700 in a bank account that earns 6% interest.
   a. How much did she have in the account 5 years ago? **$3512.11**
   b. How much will she have 5 years from now? **$6289.66**

Uses Objective H

16. A test has 15 multiple-choice questions, each with 5 options. Write the probability, using a negative exponent, of guessing
   a. all correct answers. **5^{-15}**   b. all wrong answers. **$4^{15} \cdot 5^{-15}$**

86

Lesson Master 8-7 A

LESSON MASTER 8-7 A

Questions on SPUR Objectives
See pages 543-545 for objectives.

Skills Objective A

In 1–3, evaluate the fraction.

1. $\frac{2^6}{2^2}$ 2^4, or 16   2. $\frac{3^5}{3^7}$ $\frac{1}{3^2}$, or $\frac{1}{9}$ 3. $\frac{6.8 \cdot 10^5}{1.7 \cdot 10^9}$ $\frac{4}{10^4}$, or $\frac{4}{10,000}$

Skills Objective B

4. Simplify $\frac{n^3}{n^{13}}$. Give your answer
   a. as a fraction. $\frac{1}{n^{10}}$ b. using a negative exponent. n^{-10}

In 5–11, simplify. Write answers without negative exponents.

5. $\frac{a^{10}}{a^7}$ a^3 6. $\frac{x^2}{x^{14}}$ $\frac{1}{x^{12}}$ 7. $\frac{6x}{3x^5}$ $\frac{2}{x^4}$

8. $\frac{a^3 b^5}{a^4 b^4}$ $\frac{b}{a}$ 9. $\frac{12n^3 x^{10}}{20n^6 x^2}$ $\frac{3x^8}{5n^3}$

10. $\frac{(a-6)^8}{(a-6)^9}$ $\frac{1}{a-6}$ 11. $\frac{20a^2}{2x} \cdot \frac{15x^2}{a^{10}}$ $\frac{150x}{a^8}$

Properties Objective E

12. Write an algebraic fraction that will simplify to $10n^3$ by using the Quotient of Powers Property. **Sample: $\frac{10n^8}{n^5}$**

13. Explain how to use the Quotient of Powers Property to find the value of x in $\frac{4^x}{4^6} = 4^9$.
$$\frac{4^x}{4^6} = 4^{x-6} = 4^9, \text{ so } x - 6 = 9 \text{ and } x = 15.$$

Uses Objective H

14. The North Star is about 680 light-years from Earth. A light-year is $5.879 \cdot 10^{12}$ miles. How many miles away from Earth is the North Star? Give your answer in scientific notation. **$3.9977 \cdot 10^{15}$ mi**

15. In 1992, the U.S. Internal Revenue Service collected $476 billion in individual income taxes. The U.S. population was about $2.5 \cdot 10^8$. What was the average amount of tax paid per person? **≈$1904**

87

Lesson Master 8-8 A

LESSON MASTER 8-8 A

Questions on SPUR Objectives
See pages 543-545 for objectives.

Skills Objective A

In 1–3, tell if the number is *positive* or *negative*.

1. -18^2 **negative**   2. $(-10)^3$ **negative**   3. $(-42)^4$ **positive**

In 4–9, evaluate the expression.

4. -7^2 -49 5. $(2 \cdot 10)^3$ $8,000$ 6. $\left(\frac{3}{5}\right)^3$ $\frac{27}{125}$

7. $(3^{-2})^2$ $\frac{1}{81}$ 8. $(1.4 \cdot 10^8)^5$ $5.37824 \cdot 10^{40}$ 9. $(8.95 \cdot 10^6)^3$ $7.1691738 \cdot 10^{20}$

Skills Objective C

In 10–15, simplify the expression.

10. $(3x)^4$ $81x^4$ 11. $(2a^4)^3$ $8a^{12}$

12. $\left(\frac{8}{9}ny^{10}\right)^2$ $\frac{64}{81}n^2 y^{20}$ 13. $10x \cdot (-5x^3)^3$ $-1250x^{10}$

14. $\left(\frac{6n^4}{x}\right)^2$ $\frac{36n^8}{x^2}$ 15. $\left(\frac{1}{3}x\right)^2 \cdot (6^2)^3$ $5184x^2$

Properties Objective E

16. Simplify $(ab^5)^3$ by rewriting using
   a. repeated multiplication.
$$(ab^5)^3 = ab^5 \cdot ab^5 \cdot ab^5 = a^3 b^{15}$$
   b. the Power of a Product Property.
$$(ab^5)^3 = a^3 \cdot (b^5)^3 = a^3 b^{15}$$

88   ▶

ALGEBRA © Scott, Foresman and Company

164

Page 89 (top left)

Name _____

▶ **LESSON MASTER 8-8 A** *page 2*

17. Simplify $\left(\frac{10}{n^a}\right)^4$ by rewriting using

   a. repeated multiplication.
   $$\left(\frac{10}{n^a}\right)^4 = \frac{10}{n^a} \cdot \frac{10}{n^a} \cdot \frac{10}{n^a} \cdot \frac{10}{n^a} = \frac{10,000}{n^{4a}}$$

   b. the Power of a Quotient Property.
   $$\left(\frac{10}{n^a}\right)^4 = \frac{10}{(n^a)^4} = \frac{10,000}{n^{4a}}$$

In 18–21, *multiple choice*. Name the property that is illustrated.
(a) Product of Powers   (b) Quotient of Powers
(c) Power of a Power   (d) Power of a Product
(e) Power of a Quotient

18. $(x^3)^5 = x^{15}$ **c**   19. $(3x)^5 = 243x^5$ **d**

20. $\left(\frac{n}{a^3}\right)^4 = \frac{n^4}{a^{12}}$ **e**   21. $\frac{n^4}{n^3} = n$ **b**

Uses Objective H

22. The length of one edge of each cube is given. Find the volume of each cube.

   a. x in. _____ x^3
   b. $4x$ in. _____ $64x^3$
   c. $6x$ in. _____ $216x^3$

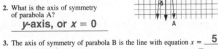

x in. $4x$ in. $6x$ in.

89

Page 90 (top right)

Name _____

Questions on SPUR Objectives
See pages 543-545 for objectives.

Uses Objective A

In 1–3, simplify, giving the answer as a simple fraction.

1. $\left(\frac{9}{13}\right)^{-1}$ $\frac{13}{9}$ 2. $\left(\frac{7}{8}\right)^{-2}$ $\frac{64}{49}$ 3. $\left(\frac{5}{3}\right)^{-3}$ $\frac{27}{125}$

4. *Multiple choice.* Which of the following equals $(4x^{-5})^{-3}$?

   (a) $64x^{15}$ (b) $\frac{64}{x^{15}}$ (c) $\frac{x^{15}}{64}$ (d) $\frac{1}{64x^{15}}$

   Explain your reasoning.
   c; sample: By the Power of a Product and Power of Powers Properties, $(4x^{-5})^{-3} =$ $4^{-3} \cdot x^{-5 \cdot -3} = \frac{x^{15}}{64}$

5. Find a counterexample for the pattern $x^2 \cdot x^4 = x^8$.
   Sample: $x = 2$, since $2^2 \cdot 2^4 = 4 \cdot 16 = 64$ and $2^8 = 256$.

Properties Objective D

6. Alicia can't remember how to simplify $\frac{x^6}{x^2}$ but she thinks the answer is x^3. For each value of x, tell if $\frac{x^6}{x^2} = x^3$ is *true* or *false*.

   a. $x = 1$ **True**   b. $x = 2$ **False**
   c. $x = 0$ **False**   d. $x = -1$ **False**

In 7–9, choose the simplified form of the given expression. **Sample** Check your answer by testing a special case. **checks are given.**

7. $2x^3 \cdot 8x^{10}$ (a) $16x^{30}$ (b) $16x^{13}$ (c) $10x^{30}$ (d) $10x^{13}$ **b**
   $x = 2$: $2 \cdot 2^3 \cdot 8 \cdot 2^{10} = 16 \cdot 2^{13} = 131,072$; $16 \cdot 2^{30}$
   $= 131,072$

8. $(5x^2)^3$ (a) $5x^5$ (b) $5x^6$ (c) $125x^5$ (d) $125x^6$ **d**
   $x = 2$: $(5 \cdot 2^2)^3 = 20^{-3} = 8000$; $125 \cdot 2^6 = 8000$

9. $\frac{x^{10}}{x^2}$ (a) x^8 (b) x^5 (c) $\frac{1}{x^8}$ (d) $\frac{1}{x^5}$ **a**
   $x = 3$: $\frac{3^{10}}{3^2} = \frac{59,049}{9} = 6561$; $3^8 = 6561$

90

Page 91 (bottom left)

Name _____

Questions on SPUR Objectives
See pages 610-613 for objectives.

Vocabulary

In 1–6, use the graphs of parabolas A and B at the right.

1. What seems to be the vertex of
   a. parabola A? _____ **(0, 0)**
   b. parabola B? _____ **(5, -2)**

2. What is the axis of symmetry of parabola A?
   y-axis, or $x = 0$

3. The axis of symmetry of parabola B is the line with equation $x =$ ___ **5**.

4. Which parabola opens   a. up? _____ **B**
      b. down? _____ **A**

5. Which parabola has a   a. maximum? _____ **A**
      b. minimum? _____ **B**

6. Give the coordinates of the point that is the reflection image of the given point over the parabola's axis of symmetry.
   a. (-2, -8) on parabola A   **(2, -8)**
   b. (3, 2) on parabola B   **(7, 2)**

Skills Objective A

In 7–9, find both values of x. If answers are not integers, round to the nearest hundredth.

7. $24.5 = .5x^2$
   $x = 7$ or $x = -7$

8. $\frac{3}{5}x^2 = 21$
   $x \approx 5.92$ or $x \approx -5.92$

9. $.02x^2 = 6.28$
   $x \approx 17.72$ or $x \approx -17.72$

91 ▶

Page 92 (bottom right)

Name _____

▶ **LESSON MASTER 9-1 A** *page 2*

In 10–12, use $d = 16t^2$, Galileo's formula relating the time t in seconds an object falls a distance d in feet.

10. How far does an object fall in 10 seconds? _____ **1600 feet**
11. How far does an object fall in $2t$ seconds? _____ **$65t^2$ feet**
12. A nail rolled off the roof of a building under construction and fell 324 feet to the ground below. How long did it take the nail to fall? _____ **4.5 seconds**

Representations Objective F:

In 13 and 14, use the given equation. Make a table of values using x-values -4, -2, -1, 0, 1, 2, and 4. Then graph the equation.

13. $y = -\frac{1}{4}x^2$

x	y
-4	-4
-2	-1
-1	$-\frac{1}{4}$
0	0
1	$-\frac{1}{4}$
2	-1
4	-4

14. $y = 3x^2$

x	y
-4	48
-2	12
-1	3
0	0
1	3
2	12
4	48

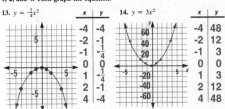

15. From the equation of a parabola, explain how to tell if its graph opens up or down. Give an example of each type of equation.
   Sample: If the equation of the parabola is $y = ax^2$, for $a < 0$ the parabola opens down ($y = -4x^2$), and for $a > 0$ the parabola opens up ($y = 3x^2$).

16. Does the parabola with equation $y = -5x^2$ have a minimum point? Why or why not?
   No; sample: In the equation $y = -5x^2$, $a < 0$ so the parabola opens down.

92

165

LESSON MASTER 9-2 A

Questions on SPUR Objectives
See pages 610-613 for objectives.

Representations Objective F

In 1 and 2, give an example of an equation of the form $y = ax^2 + bx + c$ whose graph is a parabola that opens

Samples are given.

1. up. $y = 3x^2 - 2x + 4$

2. down $y = -5x^2 + 2x + 1$

In 3 and 4, the graph of a parabola is shown.
a. Give the coordinates of the vertex.
b. Give the y-intercept.
c. Give an equation for the axis of symmetry.

3.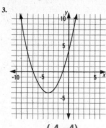

a. $(-4, -4)$
b. 4
c. $x = -4$

4.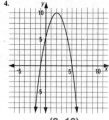

a. $(2, 10)$
b. 6
c. $x = 2$

5. a. Complete this table of values for a parabola.

x	-2	-1	0	1	2	3	4	5	6
y	23	14	7	2	-1	-2	-1	2	7

b. What are the coordinates of its vertex? $(3, -2)$

c. What is the y-intercept? 7

d. Does this parabola have a maximum value? no

e. Does this parabola open up? yes

In 6 and 7, an equation is given. a. Complete the table of values. b. Graph the equation. c. Give the coordinates of the vertex. d. Give the y-intercept. e. Write an equation for the axis of symmetry.

6. $y = x^2 + 4x + 3$

a.
x	y
-3	0
-2	-1
-1	0
0	3
1	8
2	15
3	24

b.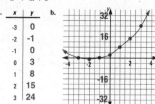

c. $(-2, -1)$
d. 3
e. $x = -2$

7. $y = -2x^2 + 4x$

a.
x	y
-3	-30
-2	-16
-1	-6
0	0
1	2
2	0
3	-6

b.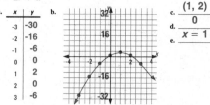

c. $(1, 2)$
d. 0
e. $x = 1$

8. a. Use symmetry to complete the graph on the right.

b. Give its y-intercept. 5

c. Give its x-intercepts. $-5, -1$

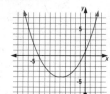

LESSON MASTER 9-3 A

Questions on SPUR Objectives
See pages 610-613 for objectives.

Representations Objective F

1.

The equation $y = x^2 - 10x + 16$ is graphed at the left.

a. Give the x-coordinate of the vertex. 5

b. Find the y-coordinate of the vertex. -9

c. Write an equation for the axis of symmetry. $x = 5$

2. a. On the default window of an automatic grapher, graph these four parabolas.

$y = x^2$ $y = x^2 - 2x$ $y = x^2 - 4x$ $y = x^2 - 6x$

b. Describe how the graphs are similar and how they are different.

Sample: Parabolas open up, seem similar, and have zero as an x-intercept; they have different vertices and axes of symmetry.

c. Describe the graph of $y = x^2 - 50x$.

Sample: It is a parabola that opens up; its axis of symmetry is $x = 25$; its vertex is $(25, -625)$; its x-intercepts are 0 and 50.

3. The graph of a parabola is $y = -x^2 + 6x + 60$. Identify a different window that shows the vertex, the y-intercept, and both x-intercepts.

A sample is given.
$-10 \le x \le 13$
$-30 \le y \le 80$

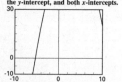

4. Use an automatic grapher to graph $y = x^2 + 4x$ and $y = -x$ on the same grid. Estimate the coordinates of the points where the graphs intersect. $(0, 0), (-5, 5)$

LESSON MASTER 9-4 A

Questions on SPUR Objectives
See pages 610-613 for objectives.

Uses Objective E

In 1-5, use the graph at the right. It illustrates the path of a football as it leaves the hands of the quarterback and is thrown to a receiver. The graph shows the height h after the ball has traveled x yards forward.

1. How far is the receiver from the quarterback? ≈ 21 yards

2. About how high is the ball when it has moved 2 yards forward? ≈ 7.7 feet

3. Is the ball ever 15 feet above the ground? no

4. At what distance(s) from the quarterback is the ball 10.5 feet above the ground? 6 yd, 15 yd

5. Most professional basketball players can reach 10 feet when they jump. Could such a person catch the ball if he were positioned 3 feet in front of the receiver? yes

In 6-10, use the graph. It shows the height h in feet of water t seconds after leaving the mouth of a fountain. The equation is $h = -6t^2 + 12t + 10$.

6. What is the greatest height the water reaches? 16 ft

7. How long is the water in the air? ≈ 2.6 sec

8. How high is the fountain's mouth? 10 ft

9. What is the height of the water after 2 seconds? 10 ft

10. Find the height of the water after 1.7 seconds. 13.06 ft

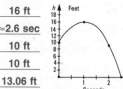

LESSON MASTER 9-5 A

Name _____

Skills Objective A

1. Write the Quadratic Formula. $x = \dfrac{-b \pm \sqrt{b^2 - 4ac}}{2a}$

In 2–5, find the two values of the expression.

2. $\dfrac{-1 \pm 5}{2}$ **-3, 2**

3. $\dfrac{15 \pm 3}{12}$ **$1, \frac{3}{2}$**

4. $\dfrac{0 \pm \sqrt{49}}{2}$ **$-\frac{7}{2}, \frac{7}{2}$**

5. $\dfrac{-6 \pm \sqrt{36 - -220}}{2}$ **-11, 5**

6. Write the equation $6x + 2x^2 = 4x^2 + 5x + 1$ in standard form. **$2x^2 - x + 1 = 0$**

In 7–10, an equation is given in standard form a. Give the values of $a, b,$ and c. b. Give the solutions rounded to the nearest hundredth.

7. $x^2 - 7x + 6 = 0$ a. **$a: 1, b: -7, c: 6$** b. **1; 6**

8. $3y^2 - 10y - 8 = 0$ a. **$a: 3, b: -10, c: -8$** b. **.67; 4**

9. $v^2 - 11v = 0$ a. **$a: 1, b: -11, c: 0$** b. **0; 11**

10. $m^2 + 7m + 2 = 0$ a. **$a: 1, b: 7, c: 2$** b. **-6.70; -.30**

In 11–13, a. rewrite the equation in standard form, and b. give the solution rounded to the nearest hundredth.

11. $b^2 + 4b = 5$ a. **$b^2 + 4b - 5 = 0$** b. **-5; 1**

12. $5(h^2 - 5h + 2) - 2h = 0$ a. **$5h^2 - 27h + 10 = 0$** b. **.40; 5**

13. $m^2 = 1 - 3m$ a. **$m^2 + 3m - 1 = 0$** b. **-3.30; .30**

14. Show that 0.5 and -3 are solutions of $4x^2 + 10x - 6 = 0$.
$4(.5)^2 + 10(.5) - 6 = 1 + 5 - 6 = 0$;
$4(-3)^2 + 10(-3) - 6 = 36 - 30 + 6 = 0$

Uses Objective E

In 15–17, use the equation $h = 60t - 16t^2 + 2$, where h is the height in feet after t seconds of a batted baseball. Round answers to the nearest tenth.

15. At what two times is the ball 20 feet in the air? **.33 sec, 3.42 sec**

16. When is the ball at 58 feet? **1.75 sec, 2 sec**

17. How long does it take for the ball to hit the ground? **3.78 sec**

LESSON MASTER 9-6 A

Name _____

Properties Objective D

How many real solutions does a quadratic equation have

1. when the discriminant is negative? **zero**

2. when the discriminant is positive? **two**

3. when the discriminant is zero? **one**

In 4–9, use the given equation. a. Find the value of the discriminant. b. Give the number of real solutions. c. Give all the real solutions to the nearest hundredth.

4. $x^2 + 3x + 1 = 0$
a. **5** b. **2** c. **-2.62; -.38**

5. $n^2 + n + 8 = 0$
a. **-31** b. **0** c. **no solutions**

6. $2a^2 + 13a + 6 = 0$
a. **121** b. **2** c. **-.5; -6**

7. $y^2 = 5(y + 2)$
a. **65** b. **2** c. **-1.53; 6.53**

8. $3x^2 + 5x + 7 = 0$
a. **-59** b. **0** c. **no solutions**

9. $y^2 + 14y + 6 = 9y + 5$
a. **21** b. **2** c. **-4.79; -.21**

10. For what value of h does $x^2 + 10x + h = 0$ have exactly one solution? **$h = 25$**

LESSON MASTER 9-7 A

Name _____

Skills Objective B

1. Use the triangles at the right.

a. Calculate AB. **$\sqrt{13}$**

b. Express AC as $2 \cdot AB$. **$2\sqrt{13}$**

c. Find PQ. **$\sqrt{52}$**

d. Use decimal approximations to verify that your answers to Parts b and c are equal. **$2\sqrt{13} \approx 7.21$ $\approx \sqrt{52}$**

2. Which of the expressions below equal $\sqrt{72}$?
(a) $2\sqrt{18}$ (b) $3\sqrt{8}$ (c) $4\sqrt{6}$ (d) $6\sqrt{2}$
a, b, d

3. a. State the Product of Square Roots Property.
For all non-negative real numbers a and b, $\sqrt{a} \cdot \sqrt{b} = \sqrt{ab}$.

b. Give an instance of this property. **Sample: $\sqrt{4} \cdot \sqrt{9} = \sqrt{36}$**

In 4–6, give the exact value of x in simplified form.

4. **$x = 3\sqrt{2}$**

5. **$x = 3\sqrt{2}$**

6. **$x = 5\sqrt{3}$**

7. a. Use the Pythagorean Theorem to write an expression for the length of the hypotenuse of the triangle. **$\sqrt{50n^2}$**
b. Simplify your answer to Part a. **$5n\sqrt{2}$**

In 8–10, simplify. Do not use a calculator.

8. $\sqrt{75} \cdot \sqrt{3}$ **15**

9. $\sqrt{9 \cdot 16}$ **12**

10. $\sqrt{12^2 \cdot 10^2}$ **120**

In 11 and 12, give the exact solution in simplified form.

11. $(3n)^2 = 360$ **$2\sqrt{10}; -2\sqrt{10}$**

12. $\frac{x}{2} = \frac{10}{x}$ **$2\sqrt{5}; -2\sqrt{5}$**

13. Simplify.
a. $\sqrt{50}$ **$5\sqrt{2}$**
b. $\sqrt{18}$ **$3\sqrt{2}$**
c. $\sqrt{50} + \sqrt{18}$ **$8\sqrt{2}$**

LESSON MASTER 9-8 A

Name _____

Skills Objective C

In 1–6, evaluate the expression.

1. $|-26|$ **26**
2. $|4|$ **4**
3. ABS $(10 - 5)$ **5**
4. $|-6 + 6|$ **0**
5. $\sqrt{(-5)^2}$ **5**
6. $|-6| + |6|$ **12**

7. Fill in the blank. For all, y, $\sqrt{y^2} =$ **$|y|$**.

In 8–10, solve and check.

8. $|n| = 35$
$n = 35,$
$n = -35$
$|35| = 35$
$|-35| = 35$

9. $|x - 6| = 10$
$x = -4,$
$x = 16$
$|-4 - 6| =$
$|-10| = 10$
$|16 - 6| =$
$|10| = 10$

10. $|m + 12| = 4$
$m = -8,$
$m = -16$
$|-8 + 12| =$
$|4| = 4$
$|-16 + 12| =$
$|-4| = 4$

Representations Objective G

11. One version of a car-engine cylinder has a diameter of 3.75 in. and must be made with a tolerance of $\pm .001$ in. This means that the diameter of the cylinders produced must not be more or less than $3.75 \pm .001$ in.

a. What is the least diameter acceptable? **3.749 in.**
b. What is the greatest diameter acceptable? **3.751 in.**
c. Should a cylinder with a diameter 3.747 be considered defective? **yes**
d. Graph all acceptable diameters on this number line.

```
  ←———•——————•——————•———→
    3.749   3.75   3.751
```

e. If d is the diameter of an acceptable cylinder, write an inequality relating $|d - 3.75|$ and .001. **$|d - 3.75| \le .001$**

In 12–13, find the distance between the given points.

12. ←——•———•——→ **18**
      -50 -32

13. ←——•———•——→ **$|-x + 2|$**
        -2   -x

In 14 and 15, give the coordinates of the two points on the number line that are

14. 15 units from the point with coordinate 4. **19   -11**

15. 20 units from the point with coordinate -32. **-12   -52**

LESSON MASTER 9-9 A

Questions on SPUR Objectives
See pages 610-613 for objectives.

Representations Objective G

In 1 and 2, each square represents a city block. Find the number of blocks it takes to travel from X to Y
a. if you travel on the streets and must go by way of Z, or b. if you travel "as the crow flies."

1.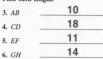

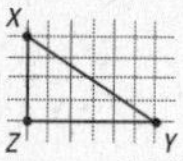

a. **10 blocks**

b. **≈7.2 blocks**

2.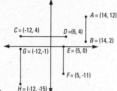

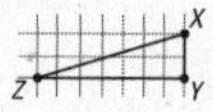

a. **9 blocks**

b. **≈7.3 blocks**

In 3–6, use the diagram at the right. Find each length.

3. AB **10**

4. CD **18**

5. EF **11**

6. GH **14**

$A = (14, 12)$
$C = (-12, 4)$ $D = (6, 4)$
$B = (14, 2)$
$G = (-12, -1)$ $E = (5, 0)$
$F = (5, -11)$
$H = (-12, -15)$

7. In the diagram, $P = (3, -1)$. Points A, B, C, and D are each 5 units from P on the horizontal or vertical line through P. Give the coordinates of each point.

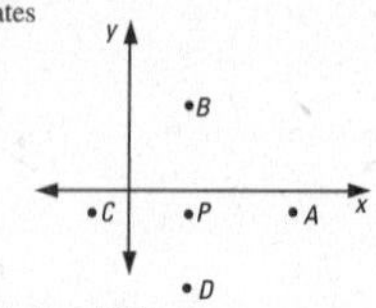

A **(8, -1)**

B **(3, 4)**

C **(-2, -1)**

D **(3, -6)**

• B
• C • P • A x
• D

8. Find the coordinates of P shown in the diagram at the right.

$P = (-6, 3)$

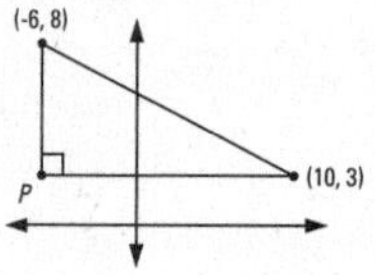

$(-6, 8)$

P $(10, 3)$

101 ▶

▶ **LESSON MASTER 9-9 A** *page 2*

9. a. Find the coordinates of Q.   **$Q = (-5, -6)$**

b. Find AQ.   **7**

c. Find BQ.   **17**

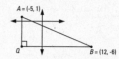
$A = (-5, 1)$
Q $B = (12, -6)$

d. Use the Pythagorean Theorem to find AB.   **$\sqrt{338}$, or ≈18.4**

10. Write a formula for the distance between (a, b) and (j, k).

Sample: **$d = \sqrt{(a - j)^2 + (b - k)^2}$**

In 11–14, use the distance formula to find the distance between the two points. Round answers to the nearest hundredth.

11. $(9, 3), (15, 11)$ **10**

12. $(-10, 12), (14, 2)$ **26**

13. $(12, -14), (15, -7)$ **≈7.6**

14. $(-10, 1), (-7, 4)$ **≈4.2**

In 15–19, use the map at the right. It shows streets and the locations of three buildings in a town. The streets are 1 block apart.

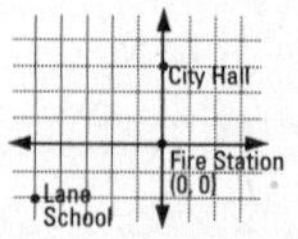

15. What are the coordinates of

a. City Hall?   **(0, 3)**

b. Lane School?   **(-5, -2)**

16. How far is it from City Hall to Fire Station?   **3 blocks**

17. How far is it from Lane School to Fire Station "as the crow flies"?   **$\sqrt{29}$, or ≈5.4, bl.**

18. How far is it from Lane School to City Hall "as the crow flies"?   **$5\sqrt{2}$, or ≈7.1, bl.**

19. How far is it to drive from City Hall to Lane School?   **10 blocks**

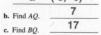
City Hall
Fire Station
(0, 0)
Lane School

102

LESSON MASTER 10-1 A

Questions on SPUR Objectives
See pages 661-663 for objectives.

Properties Objective E

1. After being simplified, which two of these expressions are binomials?   **b and c**

(a) $x + 3x$ (b) $2(y^2 + 9)$ (c) $n + 3$ (d) $5a^2$

2. Give the degree of   a. $6x^4$.   **4**   b. x^2y^5.   **7**

3. Give an example of a monomial of degree 6 in which

a. the only variable is x.   Sample: **$-4x^2$**

b. there are two variables, x and y.   Sample: **$3xy^5$**

4. a. What is the degree of the monomial 12?   **0**

b. Give an example of another monomial with the same degree as 12.   Sample: **9**

In 5–7, give the degree of the polynomial.

5. $x^5 - 2x^7$ **7**

6. $5n^2 + 7mn - 3$ **2**

7. $2x^4 + 5x^4 - 3x^6$ **6**

8. Give an example of a trinomial of degree 5.   Sample: **$x^5 + xy - 4$**

Properties Objective F

In 9 and 10, write as a polynomial in base 10.

9. 7,007,007   **$7 \cdot 10^6 + 7 \cdot 10^3 + 7$**

10. 2,358   **$2 \cdot 10^3 + 3 \cdot 10^2 + 5 \cdot 10 + 8$**

11. Simplify $3 \cdot 10^5 + 4 \cdot 10^3 + 2 \cdot 10^2 + 3 \cdot 10^1$.   **304,230**

Representations Objective I

12. Express the area of the figure as a polynomial.

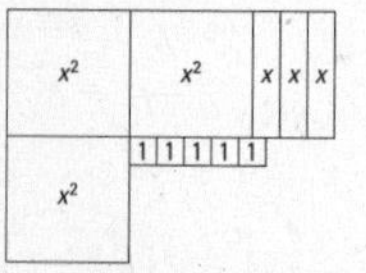

$3x^2 + 3x + 5$

13. Make a drawing to represent $2x + 6$. Use a rectangular arrangement of algebra tiles.

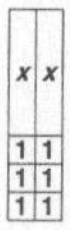

103

LESSON MASTER 10-2 A

Questions on SPUR Objectives
See pages 661-663 for objectives.

Skills Objective A

In 1–4, simplify the expression.

1. $(8x^2 + 5x - 4) + (6x^2 + 2x - 3)$ **$14x^2 + 7x - 7$**

2. $(5a^2 - 6a + 1) - (2a^2 - 3a - 2)$ **$3a^2 - 3a + 3$**

3. $(3n^2 - 5n) - (n^2 + 2n - 8)$ **$2n^2 - 7n + 8$**

4. $(m^2 + 3m - 12) + (m^2 - 8m + 3)$ **$2m^2 - 5m - 9$**

Uses Objective G

5. James Garcia won the lottery and will receive $25,000 on June 1st each year for four years. He is planning to invest the money.

a. Suppose James saves all the prize money, investing it in an account that earns interest at a scale factor x. Complete the table to show how much James will have on June 1 of each year. (Remember that the payments continue for only 4 years, although the money continues to earn interest.)

YEAR	AMOUNT
1	25,000
2	$25,000x + 25,000$
3	$25,000x^2 + 25,000x + 25,000$
4	$25,000x^3 + 25,000x^2 + 25,000x + 25,000$
5	$25,000x^4 + 25,000x^3 + 25,000x^2 + 25,000x + 25,000$
6	$25,000x^5 + 25,000x^4 + 25,000x^3 + 25,000x^2 + 25,000x + 25,000$

b. Calculate how much James would have the sixth year if his interest rate were 5%.   **$118,797.82**

c. How much he would have the sixth year if he could find an investment earning 12%?   **$149,879.73**

d. Suppose the yearly prize had been $250,000 instead of $25,000. Explain how to use the Distributive Property and your answer to Part **c** to easily find out how much he would have the sixth year earning 12% if he saved all his prize money.

Sample: **The coefficient of each term for 6 years is 10 times as great, so multiply the 6-year sum by 10.**

104   ▶

▶ **LESSON MASTER 10-2 A** *page 2*

In 8–10, use this information: Amy and Anton have just graduated and are each saving money for a down payment on a house. They will each deposit their savings into a special account earning 5.5% interest compounded annually. Their plans are described below.

Amy: Wait and deposit $5,000 at the beginning of the 6th, 7th, and 8th years.

Anton: Deposit $4,000 at the beginning of the 1st, 2nd, and 3rd years.

8. Complete the spreadsheet below.

	A	B	C	D	E
1	Year	Amy's Deposit	Amy's End of Year Balance	Anton's Deposit	Anton's End of Year Balance
2	1	0	**0**	4,000	**4,220**
3	2	0	**0**	4,000	8,672.10
4	3	0	**0**	4,000	**13,369.07**
5	4	0	**0**	0	**14,104.36**
6	5	0	**0**	0	**14,880.10**
7	6	5,000	**5,275**	0	**15,698.51**
8	7	5,000	**10,840.13**	0	**16,561.93**
9	8	5,000	**16,711.34**	0	**17,472.83**

9. What formula could be used to calculate the value in

a. cell C9? **Samples: =1.055*(C8+B9)**
B7*(1.055^3+1.055^2+1.055)

b. cell E9? **Samples: =1.055*E8**
D2*(1.055^8+1.055^7+1.055^6)

10. Who has more money at the end of 8 years? How much more?
Anton; $761.49

LESSON MASTER **10-3 A**

Questions on SPUR Objectives
See pages 661-663 for objectives.

Skills Objective C

In 1–10, simplify the expression.

1. $3(x + 5)$ **$3x + 15$**

2. $2y(3y^2 + 10y - 6)$ **$6y^3 + 20y^2 - 12y$**

3. $4x(2x)$ **$8x^2$**

4. $4x(2 + x)$ **$4x^2 + 8x$**

5. $-4ab(a^2 - 6ab + 9)$ **$-4a^3b + 24a^2b^2 - 36ab$**

6. $2m^4(m^5 - 3)$ **$2m^9 - 6m^4$**

7. $8(x + 9) + x$ **$9x + 72$**

8. $3(x^2 + 4x) + x(x - 15)$ **$4x^2 - 3x$**

9. $n(2n + 9) - 6(n - 1)$ **$2n^2 + 3n + 6$**

10. $x(2a + 1) + 6a(-x + 9)$ **$-4ax + x + 54a$**

In 11–14, fill in the blank.

11. $2(x + \underline{\textbf{9}}) = 2x + 18$

12. $6n(\underline{\dfrac{\textbf{4n}}{}} + 9) = 24n^2 + 54n$

13. $x^2(x^2 + \underline{\textbf{y}}) = x^4 + x^2y$

14. $\underline{\textbf{-3}}(2y + 7) = -6y - 21$

Representations Objective I

In 15–16, a rectangle is shown. a. Express the area as length • width. b. Express the area as the sum of smaller areas. c. Write an equation using the expressions from parts a and b for the area of the rectangle.

15.

a. **$(2x + 2)x$**

b. **$2x^2 + 2x$**

c. **$(2x + 2)x = 2x^2 + 2x$**

16.

a. **$(2x + 3)2x$**

b. **$4x^2 + 6x$**

c. **$(2x + 3)2x = 4x^2 + 6x$**

LESSON MASTER **10-4 A**

Questions on SPUR Objectives
See pages 661-663 for objectives.

Skills Objective B

In 1–5, multiply and simplify.

1. $(n + 3)(n^2 + 5n + 9)$
$n^3 + 8n^2 + 24n + 27$

2. $(y - 2)(5y^2 + y - 4)$
$5y^3 - 9y^2 - 6y + 8$

3. $(x^2 + 2x + 3)(4x^2 - 8x + 1)$
$4x^4 - 3x^2 - 22x + 3$

4. $(5m + x - 1)(m - 6x - 8)$
$5m^2 - 6x^2 - 29mx - 41m - 2x + 8$

5. $(x + 8)(x + 3)(x - 2)$ **$x^3 + 9x^2 + 2x - 48$**

Representations Objective I

6. a. Express the area of the large rectangle as length · width.
$(5 + a + b)(b + a + 2)$

b. Express this area as the sum of nine smaller areas.

$a^2 + b^2 + ab + ab + 2a + 5a + 2b + 5b + 10$

7. A cube has edges 5 cm long. A larger cube had edges a cm longer.

a. What is the volume of the first cube? **125 cm^3**

b. What is the volume of the larger cube? **$(x^3 + 15x^2 + 75x + 125)\text{ cm}^3$**

c. How much greater is the volume of the larger cube than the volume of the smaller one? **$(x^3 + 15x^2 + 75x)\text{ cm}^3$**

8. a. Write an expression for the volume of the box at the right.
$2x^3 + 9x^2 + 10x + 3$

b. Check your answer to Part **a** by substituting 6 for x.

Dimensions are 13, 7, and 9, with volume
819; $2(6^3) + 9(6^2) + 10(6) + 3 = 819$

LESSON MASTER **10-5 A**

Questions on SPUR Objectives
See pages 661-663 for objectives.

Skills Objective C

In 1–7, multiply and simplify.

1. $(n + 8)(n + 2)$ **$n^2 + 10n + 16$**

2. $(x - 6)(x + 8)$ **$x^2 + 2x - 48$**

3. $(y - 3)(y - 9)$ **$y^2 - 12y + 27$**

4. $(4a + 5)(4a - 5)$ **$16a^2 - 25$**

5. $(a - b)(a + 5b)$ **$a^2 + 4ab - 5b^2$**

6. $(n^2 + 2n)(n + 5)$ **$n^3 + 7n^2 + 10n$**

7. $(3 + \sqrt{5})(10 - \sqrt{5})$ **$25 + 7\sqrt{5}$**

In 8 and 9, fill in the blanks.

8. $(n + 2)(n - \underline{\textbf{7}}) = n^2 - 5n - 14$

9. $(x + \underline{\textbf{1}})(x + 6) = x^2 + 7x + 6$

Representations Objective I

In 10 and 11, two binomials are given. a. Simplify the product. b. Draw a diagram to represent the multiplication.

10. $(x + 5)(x + 4)$

a. **$x^2 + 9x + 20$**

b.

11. $(2x + 3)(2x + 1)$

a. **$4x^2 + 8x + 3$**

b.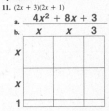

12. A fountain is in the shape of a rectangle 20 ft long and 8 ft wide. A sidewalk x feet wide surrounds the fountain.

a. What is the length of the outer rectangle? **$(2x + 20)$ ft**

b. What is the width of the outer rectangle? **$(2x + 8)$ ft**

c. Write an expression for the combined area of the fountain and the sidewalk. **$4x^2 + 56x + 160$**

Name _____

LESSON MASTER 10-6 A

Questions on SPUR Objectives
See pages 661-663 for objectives.

Skills Objective C

In 1–9, multiply and simplify.

1. $(x + 7)(x + 4)$ **2.** $(3m - 5)(m + 3)$ **3.** $(d - 3)(2d - 7)$

$x^2 + 11x + 28$ $3m^2 + 4m - 15$ $2d^2 - 13d + 21$

4. $(2a + 6)(3a - 9)$ **5.** $(x - y)(2x + 2y)$ **6.** $(n + 3a)(n - 4a)$

$6a^2 - 54$ $2x^2 - 2y^2$ $n^2 - na - 12a^2$

7. $(n - 6)(n + 6)$ **8.** $(5a + 2b)(5a - 2b)$ **9.** $(4 + \sqrt{3})(4 - \sqrt{3})$

$n^2 - 36$ $25a^2 - 4b^2$ 13

10. a. Write the Difference of Two Squares Pattern.

$a^2 - b^2 = (a + b)(a - b)$

b. Give an instance of the Difference of Two Squares Pattern.

Sample: $49 - 25 = (7 + 5)(7 - 5)$

11. Why is $x^2 + 9$ *not* a difference of two squares?

Sample: $x^2 + 9 = x^2 - (-9)$; -9 is not a square.

12. Why is $y^2 - 11$ *not* a difference of two squares?

11 is not a square.

13. Explain how you could use the Difference of Two Squares Pattern to calculate $101 \cdot 99$ mentally.

$101 \cdot 99 = (100 + 1)(100 - 1) = 100^2 - 1^2 =$
$10,000 - 1 = 9,999$

Skills Objective D

14. According to the Perfect Square Pattern, $(n + k)^2 =$ $n^2 + 2nk + k^2$

15. According to the Perfect Square Pattern, $(m - y)^2 =$ $\dfrac{m^2 - 2my}{+ y^2}$

109 ▶

Name _____

▶ **LESSON MASTER 10-6 A** *page 2*

16. Expand $(n + 5)^2$ by

a. rewriting the expression as a multiplication of $n + 5$ by itself and using the FOIL algorithm.

$(n + 5)(n + 5) = n^2 + 5n + 5n + 25 = n^2 + 10n + 25$

b. using the Perfect Square Pattern.

$(n + 5)^2 = n^2 + 2 \cdot n \cdot 5 + 5^2 = n^2 + 10n + 25$

In 17–20, expand and simplify.

17. $(4x + 1)^2$ **18.** $(2n - 9)^2$

$16x^2 + 8x + 1$ $4n^2 - 36n + 81$

19. $(8 + \sqrt{2})^2$ **20.** $(n - w)^2 + (n + w)^2$

$66 + 16\sqrt{2}$ $2n^2 + 2w^2$

Representations Objective I

21. a. Express the area of the figure at the right as the square of a binomial.

$(x + 3)^2$

b. Express the area as the sum of smaller areas.

$x^2 + 6x + 9$

For 22 and 23, an expression is given. **a.** Draw a figure whose area is given by the expression. **b.** Write the polynomial represented by your drawing in Part a.

22. $(x + 4)^2$ **23.** $(3x + 2)^2$

a.   **a.**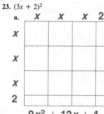

b. $x^2 + 8x + 16$ **b.** $9x^2 + 12x + 4$

110

Name _____

LESSON MASTER 10-7 A

Questions on SPUR Objectives
See pages 661-663 for objectives.

Uses Objective H

In 1 and 2, use the following information and the chi-square critical-value table given below.

A psychologist wanted to see whether people associated particular colors with musical selections. He performed an experiment in which he played a musical selection and then asked each listener which one of the following four colors they associated with that selection. His results are listed in the table.

Colors	Percent of Listeners Choosing Color
Red	19%
Blue	21%
Green	24%
Yellow	36%

1. Suppose the psychologist had questioned 80 people.

a. Find the number of people choosing each color.

Red _____ 15 _____ Blue _____ 17 _____

Green _____ 19 _____ Yellow _____ 29 _____

b. The psychologist believes that there is no tendency for people to associate any particular color with the music. How many people would then be expected to choose each color?

Red _____ 20 _____ Blue _____ 20 _____

Green _____ 20 _____ Yellow _____ 20 _____

c. Use the actual numbers and the psychologist's expected numbers to calculate the chi-square statistic for this experiment. _____ 5.8 _____

111 ▶

Name _____

▶ **LESSON MASTER 10-7 A** *page 2*

	Critical Chi-Square Values			
$n - 1$	.10	.05	.01	.001
1	2.71	3.84	6.63	10.8
2	4.61	5.99	9.21	13.8
3	6.25	7.81	11.34	16.3
4	7.78	9.49	13.28	18.5
5	9.24	11.07	15.09	20.5
6	10.6	12.6	16.8	22.5
7	12.0	14.1	18.5	24.3
8	13.4	15.5	20.1	26.1
9	14.7	16.9	21.7	27.9
10	16.0	18.3	23.2	29.6

d. Refer to the Critical Chi-Square Values table above. Using your answer to Part c, what can you conclude about the psychologist's belief?

Sample: The psychologist's belief is invalid, as there is a greater than 10% chance the results would occur in the equally-likely cases.

2. Suppose the psychologist had asked 200 people. Answer the same questions that you did for Question 1 for 200 people.

a. Red _____ 38 _____ Blue _____ 42 _____

Green _____ 48 _____ Yellow _____ 72 _____

b. Red _____ 50 _____ Blue _____ 50 _____

Green _____ 50 _____ Yellow _____ 50 _____

c. _____ 13.92 _____

d. Sample: The psychologist's belief is valid, as there is less than 1% chance the results would occur in the equally-likely cases.

3. From Questions 1 and 2, what can you say about the relationship between sample size and the conclusions reached in the experiment?

Sample: Because the chi-square value is greater for a greater sample size, it is more likely that the conclusions are correct.

112

LESSON MASTER 11-1 A

Representations Objective H

1. a. Use a brace ({) to write the system of equations shown on this graph.

$$\begin{cases} x + y = 0 \\ y = 1.5x - 10 \end{cases}$$

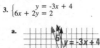

b. What is the solution to the system?

$(4, -4)$

c. Write a check to show that your answer to Part **b** is a solution to the system from Part **a**.

$4 + (-4) = 0, 0 = 0;$

$-4 = 1.5 \cdot (4) - 10, -4 = -4$

In 2 and 3, a system is given. **a.** Graph the two lines. **b.** Give the solution. **c.** If there is a solution, check it.

2. $\begin{cases} y = x + 1 \\ y = -2x + 4 \end{cases}$

a.

$y = -2x + 4$ (1, 2)
$y = x + 1$

b. $(1, 2)$

c. $2 \stackrel{?}{=} 1 + 1, 2 = 2;$
$2 \stackrel{?}{=} -2 \cdot 1 + 4; 2 = 2$

3. $\begin{cases} y = -3x + 4 \\ 6x + 2y = 2 \end{cases}$

a.
$y = -3x + 4$
$6x + 2y = 2$

b. no solution

c. _____

LESSON MASTER 11-2 A

Skills Objective A

In 1 and 2, tell if the given point is the solution of the system.

1. $(6, 9)$ $\begin{cases} y = 4x - 15 \\ y = \frac{1}{2}x - 3 \end{cases}$ no

2. $x = 15, y = 11$ $\begin{cases} y = \frac{2}{3}x + 1 \\ y = x - 4 \end{cases}$ yes

In 3-6, solve the system using substitution and check your results.

3. $\begin{cases} y = -4x + 32 \\ y = x - 3 \end{cases}$
$(7, 4)$
$4 \stackrel{?}{=} -4 \cdot 7 + 32, 4 = 4;$
$4 \stackrel{?}{=} 7 - 3, 4 = 4$

4. $\begin{cases} h = v + 5 \\ h = -\frac{1}{2}v + 2 \end{cases}$
$(-2, 3)$
$3 \stackrel{?}{=} -2 + 5, 3 = 3;$
$3 \stackrel{?}{=} -\frac{1}{2}(-2) + 2, 3 = 3$

5. $\begin{cases} d = r + 1 \\ d = -2r - 2 \end{cases}$
$(-1, 0)$
$0 \stackrel{?}{=} -1 + 1, 0 = 0;$
$0 \stackrel{?}{=} -2(-1) - 2; 0 = 0$

6. $\begin{cases} y = \frac{1}{2}x - 2 \\ y = \frac{3}{2}x - 7 \end{cases}$
$(5, \frac{1}{2})$
$\frac{1}{2} \stackrel{?}{=} \frac{1}{2}(5) - 2, \frac{1}{2} = \frac{1}{2};$
$\frac{1}{2} \stackrel{?}{=} \frac{3}{2}(5) - 7, \frac{1}{2} = \frac{1}{2}$

Uses Objective F

7. A river is flooded and the height of the water is rising. The levee along the river is 30 feet high and workers are building it higher at the rate of $\frac{1}{2}$ ft per hour. The water height is 28 feet and it is rising $\frac{3}{4}$ ft each hour.

a. Describe this situation with a system of equations.

$\begin{cases} y = 30 + \frac{1}{2}x \\ y = 28 + \frac{3}{4}x \end{cases}$

b. Solve the system to find when the water will reach the top of the levee if these rates continue.

$(8, 34);$ in 8 hr

c. If, in fact, the water stops rising after 12 hours, will it rise above the levee and cause a flood?

yes

LESSON MASTER 11-3 A

Skills Objective A

In 1-6, solve the system by substitution. Check the solution.

1. $\begin{cases} y = x + 4 \\ 2x + y = 1 \end{cases}$
$(-1, 3)$
$3 \stackrel{?}{=} -1 + 4, 3 = 3;$
$2(-1) + 3 \stackrel{?}{=} 1, 1 = 1$

2. $\begin{cases} y = 2x \\ 7x + 5y = 34 \end{cases}$
$(2, 4)$
$4 \stackrel{?}{=} 2(2), 4 = 4;$
$7(2) + 5(4) \stackrel{?}{=} 34;$
$34 = 34$

3. $\begin{cases} x = y - 3 \\ 4x + 2y = 6 \end{cases}$
$(0, 3)$
$0 \stackrel{?}{=} 3 - 3, 0 = 0;$
$4(0) + 2(3) \stackrel{?}{=} 6, 6 = 6$

4. $\begin{cases} y = 2x - 8 \\ x - y = 3 \end{cases}$
$(5, 2)$
$2 \stackrel{?}{=} 2(5) - 8, 2 = 2;$
$5 - 2 \stackrel{?}{=} 3, 3 = 3$

5. $\begin{cases} x + y = 15 \\ x - y = 7 \end{cases}$
$(11, 4)$
$11 + 4 \stackrel{?}{=} 15, 15 = 15;$
$11 - 4 \stackrel{?}{=} 7, 7 = 7$

6. $\begin{cases} x - y = 3 \\ 2x - 3y = -1 \end{cases}$
$(10, 7)$
$10 - 7 \stackrel{?}{=} 3, 3 = 3;$
$2(10) - 3(7) \stackrel{?}{=} -1,$
$-1 = -1$

Uses Objective F

7. A theater sells children's tickets for $4 and adult tickets for $7. One night 575 tickets worth $3575 were sold. How many adults and how many children bought tickets?

425 ad., 150 ch.

8. Students are chosen for a scholarship based on their scores on tests of mathematics and verbal achievement. A student's qualifying score is found by doubling his verbal score and adding his math score. Gretchen's math score was 54 points higher than her verbal score. Her qualifying score was 1782. Find Gretchen's math and verbal scores.

math, 630; ver. 576

9. Huey, Dewey, and Louie want model rockets so each one is saving his allowance. Huey says, "I have 5 more dollars than you do, Louie." Dewey says, "I have twice as much as you do, Louie." Louie says, "Together we have $31.00. That's enough to buy a rocket." How much does each have?

H, $11.50; D, $13; L, $6.50

LESSON MASTER 11-4 A

Skills Objective B

In 1 and 2, write the equation that results when the left sides and the right sides of the two equations are added.

1. $\begin{cases} 4x + 3y = 8 \\ x - 3y = 22 \end{cases}$ $5x = 30$

2. $\begin{cases} -5x + 3y = 16 \\ 5x - 10y = 12 \end{cases}$ $-7y = 28$

In 3-8, solve the system. Check your solution.   Checks are not shown.

3. $\begin{cases} x + y = 30 \\ x - y = 6 \end{cases}$
$(18, 12)$

4. $\begin{cases} -10a + 7b = 25 \\ 10a + 5b = 35 \end{cases}$
$(1, 5)$

5. $\begin{cases} 2x + y = 4 \\ x - y = 2 \end{cases}$
$(2, 0)$

6. $\begin{cases} 4n + 3m = 11 \\ 4n + 5m = 5 \end{cases}$
$(5, -3)$

7. $\begin{cases} 3t + 2u = 7 \\ -2t + 2u = -2 \end{cases}$
$(\frac{9}{5}, \frac{4}{5})$

8. $\begin{cases} -2x - 3y = 4 \\ 2x - 4y = 3 \end{cases}$
$(-\frac{1}{2}, -1)$

Uses Objective F

9. At a concession stand, two pretzels and two boxes of popcorn cost $3.50. Two pretzels and four boxes of popcorn cost $6.00. Find the cost of each item.

pr., $0.50; p.c.,$1.25

10. Beth and Carol had dinner at a cafe. The total bill was $14.40. Beth's meal cost $2.00 more than Carol's. Find the cost of each person's meal.

B, $8.20; C, $6.20

11. When Rosa flew from Boston to Cleveland, the plane was going against the wind and traveled only 120 mph. However, on the return trip, the plane traveled with the wind at 230 mph. What was the plane's speed without wind? What was the average speed of the wind?

plane, 175 mph; wind, 55 mph

LESSON MASTER 11-5 A

Questions on SPUR Objectives
See pages 715-717 for objectives.

Skills Objective C

1. Solve the system $\begin{cases} x - 2y = 1 \\ 4x + y = 22 \end{cases}$

   a. by multiplying and adding to eliminate y. **(5, 2)**

   b. by multiplying and adding to eliminate x. **(5, 2)**

2. Consider the system $\begin{cases} 5a - 4b = 14 \\ 2a + 3b = 1 \end{cases}$

   a. Tell what to multiply each equation by to eliminate a. **1st: -2; 2nd: 5**

   b. Tell what to multiply each equation by to eliminate b. **1st: 3; 2nd: 4**

   c. Solve the system and check your solution. **(2, -1) Checks are not given.**

In 3–8, solve the system, and check your solution.

3. $\begin{cases} 2e + 3f = 18 \\ 5e - f = 11 \end{cases}$ **(3, 4)**

4. $\begin{cases} 2x + 6y = -2 \\ 5x - 3y = 31 \end{cases}$ **(5, -2)**

5. $\begin{cases} 10x + 3y = 23 \\ 5x + 12y = 22 \end{cases}$ **(2, 1)**

6. $\begin{cases} 4w + 5z = 7 \\ 6w - 2z = -18 \end{cases}$ **(-2, 3)**

7. $\begin{cases} 3m + 2n = 10 \\ 2m + 5n = 3 \end{cases}$ **(4, -1)**

8. $\begin{cases} -8r + 3s = 10 \\ 10r - 2s = -2 \end{cases}$ **(1, 6)**

Uses Objective F

9. A manager of an apartment building needs to buy 45 air conditioners, one for each apartment. She has planned to spend $6,000 on the air conditioners. Two models are available, one at $110 and the other at $160. How many of each should she buy to spend $6,000? **$110, 24; $160, 21**

10. For Mother's Day a florist sells two bouquets. A bouquet of 5 roses and 10 carnations costs $8.75. A larger bouquet has a dozen roses and 15 carnations. It costs $16.50. Find the cost of one rose and of one carnation. **rose, $0.75; car., $0.50**

LESSON MASTER 11-6 A

Questions on SPUR Objectives
See pages 715-717 for objectives.

Properties Objective E

1. The line $y = -4x + 5$ is parallel to which two of the following lines? **b and c**

   (a) $y = 3x + 5$ (b) $y = -4x + 3$ (c) $4x + y = 3$

2. a. Explain how to tell if two lines in a system are parallel. **Sample: The lines are parallel if their slopes are equal.**

   b. Are the lines in this system parallel? $\begin{cases} 6x - 2y = 8 \\ -15x + 10y = 30 \end{cases}$ **no**

3. Consider the system $\begin{cases} y = 3x + 2 \\ 9x - 3y = -6 \end{cases}$

   a. Find three ordered pairs that are solutions to $y = 3x + 2$. **Samples: (-1, -1), (0, 2), (2, 8)**

   b. Show that each ordered pair from Part a is also a solution to $9x - 3y = -6$. **9(-1) − 3(-1) = -6; 9(0) − 3(2) = -6; 9(2) − 3(8) = -6**

   c. How many solutions does this system have? **infinitely many**

In 4–7, tell if the system has *no solutions, one solution,* or *infinitely many solutions.*

4. $\begin{cases} 2x - 5y = 7 \\ 4x - 10y = 14 \end{cases}$ **inf. many**

5. $\begin{cases} 4a - b = -13 \\ 2a + 10b = 46 \end{cases}$ **one sol.**

6. $\begin{cases} 10x + 6y = 18 \\ 3y = 2 - 5x \end{cases}$ **no sol.**

7. $\begin{cases} 2(x + 3) = y \\ 4x - y = 9 \end{cases}$ **one sol.**

Uses Objective F

8. When Gary Liu stands on a scale with his dog Daisy, their combined weight is 173 lb. When Gary stands on the scale alone, his weight is 173 lb less Daisy's weight.

   a. Write a system of equations to describe this situation. **$G + D = 173$ $G = 173 - D$**

   b. How many solutions does this system have? **infinitely many**

► LESSON MASTER 11-6 A page 2

Representations Objective H

In 9 and 10, a system of equations is given. a. Graph the system. b. Give the solution.

9. $\begin{cases} y = 3x + 5 \\ y = 3x - 1 \end{cases}$

a.

b. **no solution**

10. $\begin{cases} 6x + 3y = -12 \\ y = -2x - 4 \end{cases}$

a.

b. **infinitely many solutions**

In 11–13, a. give a system of two equations with the indicated number of solutions, and b. graph the system. **Samples are given.**

11. one

a. $\begin{cases} x = y \\ y = 2 \end{cases}$

b.

12. none

a. $\begin{cases} y = x + 1 \\ y = x + 3 \end{cases}$

b.

13. infinitely many

a. $\begin{cases} y = x + 3 \\ 2y = 2x + 6 \end{cases}$

b.

LESSON MASTER 11-7 A

Questions on SPUR Objectives
See pages 715-717 for objectives.

Properties Objective D

1. a. Add $8x$ to both sides of $3 - 8x > 1 - 8x$. What sentence results? **3 > 1**

   b. Describe the solutions to $3 - 8x > 1 - 8x$. **all real numbers**

Multiple choice. In 2–5, tell if the sentence is

(a) *sometimes true.* (b) *always true.* (c) *never true.*

2. $3y + 6 = 3(y + 2)$ **b**

3. $n + 6 < n + 2$ **c**

4. $x - 9 = 9 - x$ **a**

5. $12 - 2x < -2(x - 6)$ **c**

In 6 and 7, give an example of an inequality that **Samples are given.**

6. has no solution. **$5x > 5x + 1$**

7. is true for all real numbers. **$x - 1 < x + 1$**

In 8 and 9, solve.

8. $3 + 15x = 3 + 2x$ **$x = 0$**

9. $\frac{1}{3}(12x - 9) < (x + 9) - (6 - 3x)$ **$x =$ all real numbers**

Uses Objective F

10. Listed below are the price plans for boxes of computer disks sold by four mail-order companies.

   A: $1.75 per box plus $5.00 shipping fee, labels included
   B: $2.00 per box plus $3.00 shipping fee, labels included
   C: $2.00 per box plus $5.00 shipping fee, labels included
   D: $1.75 per box plus $3.00 shipping fee plus $.25 per box for labels

   a. Let $x =$ number of boxes of disks ordered. Write an expression for the cost of x boxes of disks (with labels) from each company.

   A **$1.75x + 5$** B **$2x + 3$**
   C **$2x + 5$** D **$1.75x + 3 + .25x$**

   b. When does A charge more than B? **when $x < 8$**

   c. When does B charge more than C? **never**

   d. When are the costs from B and D the same? **always**

LESSON MASTER 11-8 A

Questions on SPUR Objectives
See pages 715-717 for objectives.

Uses Objective G

1. A family plans to spend between $20 and $30 at a carnival. Rides cost $1.50 and games are $1.00. Let x = the number of rides and y = the number of games.

a. Give two combinations of rides and games that fit within the family's budget.

Samples are given.
8 rides, 9 games
10 rides, 11 games

b. Describe this situation with a system of four inequalities.

$x \geq 0$

$y \geq 0$

$20 < 1.5x + y$

$1.5x + y < 30$

c. Graph the system at the right.

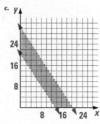

Representations Objective I

2. *Multiple choice.* Which point is a solution to $\begin{cases} y < 2x + 5 \\ y > -x + 2 \end{cases}$? __c__

(a) (1, 0) (b) (2, 9) (c) (4, -1) (d) (-1, 2)

3. Write a system of inequalities to describe points in quadrant II.

$x < 0$

$y > 0$

4. Describe the graph of $y = 0, x < 0$.

negative part of x-axis

121 ▶

▶ **LESSON MASTER 11-8 A** *page 2*

In 5–7, use the graph at the right. It is the graph of the following system of inequalities.

$$\begin{cases} y > 0 \\ y > -x + 3 \\ y < -x + 10 \end{cases}$$

Tell if the given point is a solution of the system. If not, tell which inequality it fails to satisfy.

5. (5, 8) **no; $y < -x + 10$** 6. (6, -1) **no; $y > 0$**

7. (-1, 2) **no; $y > -x + 3$**

In 8 and 9, graph the system of inequalities.

8. $\begin{cases} x > 0 \\ y > 0 \\ 2x + y < 8 \end{cases}$ 9. $\begin{cases} x < 0 \\ x > 0 \\ y > 3x - 5 \end{cases}$

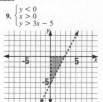

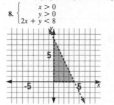

In 10 and 11, write a system of inequalities to describe the graph.

10.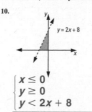

$\begin{cases} x \leq 0 \\ y \geq 0 \\ y < 2x + 8 \end{cases}$

11.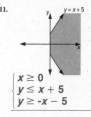

$\begin{cases} x \geq 0 \\ y \leq x + 5 \\ y \geq -x - 5 \end{cases}$

122

LESSON MASTER 12-1 A

Questions on SPUR Objectives
See pages 769-771 for objectives.

Skills Objective A

1. List all the pairs of integers whose product is 36.

1, 36; -1, -36; 2, 18; -2, -18; 3, 12; -3, -12;
4, 9; -4, -9; 6, 6; -6, -6

2. List all the pairs of integers whose product is -15.

1, -15; -1, 15; 3, -5; -3, 5

In 3–6, write the prime factorization.

3. 252 $2^2 \cdot 3^2 \cdot 7$ 4. 504 $2^3 \cdot 3^2 \cdot 7$

5. 1155 $3 \cdot 5 \cdot 7 \cdot 11$ 6. 3773 $7^3 \cdot 11$

In 7–9, determine whether or not the number is prime.

7. 127 **yes** 8. 1001 **no** 9. 2079 **no**

In 10–13, the product and the sum of a pair of integers is given. Find the numbers.

10. product: 24, sum: 11 **3, 8** 11. product: 8, sum: 9 **1, 8**

12. product: -14, sum: 5 **7, -2** 13. product: -42, sum: -1 **6, -7**

In 14–16, rewrite the fraction in lowest terms.

14. $\frac{5625}{2835}$ $\frac{125}{63}$ 15. $\frac{6768}{288}$ $\frac{47}{2}$ 16. $\frac{3024}{588}$ $\frac{36}{7}$

Properties Objective E

In 17 and 18, give the number of factors in the prime factorization.

17. 8^3 **9** 18. 7^4 **4**

19. Explain why the number $7^{20} + 7^{21} + 7^{22}$ could *not* be prime.

Sample: $7^{20} + 7^{21} + 7^{22} = 7^{20}(1 + 7 + 7^2)$,
so 7^{20} is a factor of the number.

123

LESSON MASTER 12-2 A

Questions on SPUR Objectives
See pages 769-771 for objectives.

Skills Objective B

1. List all the factors of $9x^2$. **1, 3, 9, x, $3x$, $9x$, x^2, $3x^2$, $9x^2$**

In 2–5, tell whether or not the polynomial is prime.

2. $2x + 10$ **no** 3. $n + 12$ **yes** 4. $y^2 + 15y$ **no** 5. $ab + 3y$ **yes**

In 6–9, find the greatest common factor of the monomials.

6. $18n$ and 3 **3** 7. $2x^4$ and $10x^2$ **$2x^2$**

8. d^3 and d^2 **d^2** 9. $10x^3, 15x^2$ and $20x^2y^2$ **$5x^2$**

In 10–13, fill in the blanks.

10. $12x + 20 = 4(\underline{3x} + \underline{5})$ 11. $3n^4 - 5n^3 = n^3(\underline{3n} - \underline{5})$

12. $6y^2 - 12y + 21 = 3(\underline{2y^2} + \underline{(-4y)} + \underline{7})$

13. $4a^2b + 16a^3b^2 = 4a^2b(\underline{1} + \underline{4ab})$

In 14–17, factor the polynomial completely.

14. $15x - 35$ **$5(3x - 7)$** 15. $24x^2 - 8x$ **$8x(3x - 1)$**

16. $20 - 6x + 2$ **$2(11 - 3x)$** 17. $18a^4 - a^5x$ **$a^4(18 - ax)$**

Representations Objective J

In 18 and 19, make a drawing with algebra tiles showing a rectangle that has the given area.

18. $x^2 + 3x$ 19. $2x + 8$

20. Given the fraction $\frac{3x^4 + 2x}{x}$, $(x \neq 0)$,

a. factor the numerator, and **$x(3x^3 + 2)$**

b. simplify the fraction. **$3x^3 + 2$**

124

173

LESSON MASTER 12-3 A

Skills Objective C

In 1–6, factor the expression.

1. $n^2 + 13n + 22$

$(n + 2)(n + 11)$

2. $a^2 - 5a - 14$

$(a - 7)(a + 2)$

3. $-12 + x^2 + 4x$

$(x + 6)(x - 2)$

4. $x^3 - 8x^2 + 15x$

$x(x - 3)(x - 5)$

5. $y^2 - 5y$

$y(y - 5)$

6. $x^2 - 49$

$(x + 7)(x - 7)$

Properties Objective G

7. Explain why the trinomial $x^2 + 5x + 7$ cannot be factored over the integers.

Sample: The factors of 7, 1 and 7, do not add to 5.

8. *Multiple choice.* Which polynomial can be factored over the integers?

b

(a) $x^2 - 4x + 7$ (b) $x^2 - x + 6$ (c) $x^2 + 5x - 8$ (d) $x^2 - 3x - 2$

Representations Objective J

Show that each expression can be factored by drawing a rectangle using algebra tiles.

9. $x^2 + 6x + 5$

10. $x^2 + 6x + 9$

LESSON MASTER 12-4 A

Skills Objective D

In 1–6, solve by factoring.

1. $x^2 - 2x - 15 = 0$

$x = 5$ or $x = -3$

2. $0 = x^2 - 10x + 21$

$x = 3$ or $x = 7$

3. $12m = -35 - m^2$

$m = -5$ or $m = -7$

4. $y^2 + 2y - 35 = 0$

$y = -7$ or $y = 5$

5. $h^2 + h - 42 = 0$

$h = -7$ or $h = 6$

6. $g^2 + 5g = 24$

$g = -8$ or $g = -3$

Properties Objective F

In 7–11, tell what equations result from applying the Zero Product Property.

7. $(x + 8)(x - 10) = 0$

$x + 8 = 0, \ x - 10 = 0$

8. $n(n - 3) = 0$

$n = 0, \ n - 3 = 0$

9. $x^2 + 11x + 18 = 0$

$x + 2 = 0, \ x + 9 = 0$

10. $y^2 + 12y = 0$

$y = 0, \ y + 12 = 0$

11. $(n + 3)(n + 8)(n - 7) = 0$

$n + 3 = 0, \ n + 8 = 0, \ n - 7 = 0$

Uses Objective I

12. A rectangle with area 48 cm^2 is 8 cm longer than it is wide.

  a. Write an expression for the length of the rectangle.

$w + 8$

  b. Write an equation of the form length $\cdot$ width = area.

$(w + 8)w = 48$

  c. Find the rectangle's length and width.

12 cm; 4 cm

13. A circular mirror with radius r is surrounded by a circular gilt frame 3 cm wide. If the total area of the mirror and the frame is 2025π cm^2, what is the radius of the mirror?

42 cm

LESSON MASTER 12-5 A

Skills Objective C

In 1–6, factor.

1. $2x^2 + 7x + 5$

$(2x + 5)(x + 1)$

2. $6n^2 - 7n + 2$

$(2n - 1)(3n - 2)$

3. $7x^2 + 3x - 4$

$(7x - 4)(x + 1)$

4. $13y + 6 + 5y^2$

$(5y + 3)(y + 2)$

5. $4n^2 - 4n - 3$

$(2n + 1)(2n - 3)$

6. $6a^2 - 11a - 10$

$(2a - 5)(3a + 2)$

7. Find two possible values of k for which $5x^2 + kx + 11$ can be factored, and show the factorization.

$k = -16; \ (5x - 11)(x - 1)$

$k = -56;$
$(5x - 1)(x - 11)$

8. a. Factor the greatest common factor from $10y^3 + 26y^2 - 12y$.

$2y(5y^2 + 13y - 6)$

  b. Complete the factorization of $10y^3 + 26y^2 - 12y$ by factoring the trinomial in your answer from Part a.

$2y(5y - 2)(y + 3)$

Skills Objective D

In 9–11, solve the equation. Factor when necessary.

9. $(3x - 5)(2x + 9) = 0$

$x = \frac{5}{3}$ or $x = -\frac{9}{2}$

10. $25a^2 + 30a + 9 = 0$

$a = -\frac{3}{5}$

11. $2n^2 + 5n = 12$

$n = 4$ or $n = -\frac{3}{2}$

LESSON MASTER 12-6 A

Uses Objective I

In 1 and 2, use this information: The area of a rectangular field is 9100 square meters and its perimeter is 400 meters.

1. Use the Babylonian method to find the dimensions of the field. Show your work.

$\ell + w = 200$, so let $\ell = 100 + x$ and $w = 100 - x$.
$(100 + x)(100 - x) = 9100$ $\ell = 100 + 30 = 130$
$10,000 - x^2 = 9100$ $w = 100 - 30 = 70$
$x^2 = 900$ length, 130 m;
$x = 30$ width, 70 m

2. Use a modern method to find the dimensions of the field. Show your work.

$2\ell + 2w = 400$ $\ell w = 9100$ $\ell = 130$ or $\ell = 70$
$2w = 400 - 2\ell$ $\ell(200 - \ell) = 9100$
$w = 200 - \ell$ $\ell^2 - 200\ell + 9100 = 0$
$(\ell - 130)(\ell - 70) = 0$
length, 130 m; width, 70 m

In 3 and 4, use this information: A rectangular garden covering 1500 square feet is enclosed by 160 feet of fencing.

3. Use the Babylonian method to find the dimensions of the garden. Show your work.

$\ell + w = 80$, so let $\ell = 40 + x$ and $w = 40 - x$.
$(40 + x)(40 - x) = 1500$ $\ell = 40 + 10 = 50$
$1600 - x^2 = 1500$ $w = 40 - 10 = 30$
$x^2 = 100$
$x = 10$ length, 50 ft; width, 30 ft

4. Use a modern method to find the dimensions of the garden. Show your work.

$2\ell + 2w = 160$ $\ell w = 1500$ $\ell = 50$ or $\ell = 30$
$\ell + w = 80$ $\ell(80 - \ell) = 1500$
$w = 80 - \ell$ $\ell^2 - 80\ell + 1500 = 0$
$(\ell - 50)(\ell - 30) = 0$
length, 50 ft; width, 30 ft

LESSON MASTER 12-7 A

Properties Objective H

In 1–9, tell whether the number is *rational* or *irrational*.

1. $\frac{2}{3}$ — **rational**

2. $\sqrt{2}$ — **irrational**

3. $1.\overline{3}$ — **rational**

4. 12 — **rational**

5. π — **irrational**

6. $\sqrt{25}$ — **rational**

7. $\sqrt{5}$ — **irrational**

8. 8.1 — **rational**

9. $2.7\overline{3}$ — **rational**

In 10–12, find a simple fraction equal to the number.

10. $21\frac{48}{61}$

11. 5.867

12. $13.\overline{521}$

$\dfrac{1329}{61}$　　$\dfrac{5281}{900}$　　$\dfrac{13{,}508}{999}$

13. Determine whether the solutions to the equation $4x^2 - 1 = 0$ are *rational* or *irrational*. Explain your reasoning.
rational; Sample: The solutions to
$4x^2 - 1 = 0$ **are** $x = \frac{1}{2}$ **and** $x = -\frac{1}{2}$**, both of**
which are rational numbers.

14. Can rational numbers be found in real situations? If so, give an example.
yes; Sample: The number of students in a
class

LESSON MASTER 12-8 A

Properties Objective G

1. Suppose f, g, and h are integers. How can you tell whether the polynomial $fx^2 + gx + h$ is factorable over the integers?
___$g^2 - 4fh$ **is a perfect square.**___

In 2–5, tell whether or not the polynomial is prime.

2. $6x^2 + 19x + 10$ ___**no**___

3. $5y^2 + 10y + 4$ ___**yes**___

4. $3u^2 + 13u + 14$ ___**yes**___

5. $25v + 3 + 2v^2$ ___**no**___

In 6–9, a polynomial is given. a. Calculate the discriminant of the polynomial. b. Use the discriminant to determine whether the expression can be factored over the integers.

6. $16a^2 - 18a + 9$ — a. ___**-252**___ b. ___**no**___

7. $m^2 + 15m - 17$ — a. ___**293**___ b. ___**no**___

8. $4z^2 + 15z + 5$ — a. ___**145**___ b. ___**no**___

9. $10c^2 - 29c + 10$ — a. ___**441**___ b. ___**yes**___

10. Find two integer factors of 15 whose sum is 8. What does this tell you about $x^2 + 8x + 15$?
3, 5; $x^2 + 8x + 15$ **can be factored over the**
integers.

11. Consider the polynomial $ax^2 + 7x - 15$. For what value(s) of a from 1 to 7 is the polynomial factorable?
___$a = 2, 4$___

12. The equation $y = 3x^2 + 7x - 4$ is graphed at the right. Are the x-intercepts rational? Explain your thinking.
no; Sample: The discriminant,
541, is not a perfect
square.

LESSON MASTER 13-1 A

Properties Objective C

In 1–4, explain why the equation, inequality, or set of points *does* or *does not* represent a function. **Samples are given.**

1. $y = |x|$
Yes; for each x**, there is exactly one** y**.**

2. $y < x + 3$
No; for each x**, there can be more than one** y**.**

3. $6x - 2y = 5$
Yes; for each x**, there is exactly one** y**.**

4. $\{(-3, 1), (0, 12), (2, -4), (5, 12)\}$
Yes; no two ordered pairs have same first coordinate.

5. Give a set of ordered pairs that is *not* a function.
Sample: {(5, 10), (8, -4), (5, 25)}

Representations Objectives H and I

6.
The graph of $y = \frac{1}{x}$ is shown at the left. Is this the graph of a function? Explain why or why not.
Yes; no vertical line will intersect the graph in more than one point.

In 7 and 8, a. graph the equation and b. tell if it describes a function.

7. $x = 3$
a.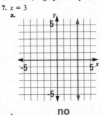
b. **no**

8. $x - y = 5$
a.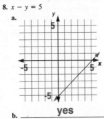
b. **yes**

LESSON MASTER 13-2 A

Vocabulary

In 1 and 2, tell how the expression or equation should be read.

1. $f(x) = x + 9$ — **f of x equals x plus nine.**

2. ABS(5) — **the absolute value of five**

Skills Objective A

In 3–6, evaluate the expression.

3. SQR(144) ___**12**___

4. $f(10)$ if $f(x) = 4x + 12$ ___**52**___

5. $f\left(\frac{7}{10}\right)$ if $f(x) = 5x$ ___$\frac{7}{2}$___

6. $g(-6)$ if $g(x) = x^2 + x + 1$ ___**31**___

7. Let $f(x) = -2x + 8$. Find
a. $f(4)$. ___**0**___
b. $f(1)$. ___**6**___
c. $\dfrac{f(4) - f(1)}{4 - 1}$. ___**-2**___

8. Suppose $f(x) = 9x - 15$. For what value of x is $f(x) = -12$? ___$x = \frac{1}{3}$___

Uses Objective E

9. A laboratory technician tested the growth of bacteria. When the experiment had been running for t hours the number of bacteria $n(t)$ was approximated by $n(t) = 250 \cdot (1.12)^t$.
a. Evaluate $n(12) - n(11)$. ___$\approx$ **104 bacteria**___
b. What does $n(12) - n(11)$ represent?
Sample: the approximate number of new cells between 11 hours and 12 hours

▶ **LESSON MASTER 13-2 A** *page 2*

10. Let $K(y)$ = Kurt's height in year y and $B(y)$ = Brad's height in year y.

a. What does it mean about the boys if $K(y) < B(y)$?

In year *y*, Kurt was shorter than Brad.

b. What does it mean if $K(y) = B(y)$?

In year *y*, Kurt and Brad were the same height.

c. What does it mean if $K(1990) < K(1991)$?

Kurt was shorter in 1990 than in 1991.

Representations Objective I

In 11 and 12, the equation of a function is given.
a. Graph the function. b. Give the y-intercept.

11. $f(x) = 4x - 8$

12. $f(x) = x^2 - 5$

a.

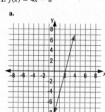

b. **-8**

a.

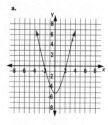

b. **-5**

133

LESSON MASTER **13-3 A** **Questions on SPUR Objectives**
See pages 821-823 for objectives.

Skills Objective A

1. If $f(x) = 2|3x + 2|$, find $f(-2)$. **8**

2. If $g(x) = -|5x|$, find $g(-1)$. **-5**

In 3 and 4, solve.

3. $|x + 2| = 3$
$x = 1$ or $x = -5$

4. $|3m - 2| + 1 = 5$
$m = 2$ or $m = -\frac{2}{3}$

Uses Objective E

5. *Multiple choice.* The actual inside diameter of certain sewer tiles is slightly more or less than 0.8 meter. Let $f(d)$ = the error in a tile with inside diameter d. Which equation relates $f(d)$ and d? **b**

(a) $f(d) = |d|$ (b) $f(d) = |0.8 - d|$ (c) $f(d) = -|d + 0.8|$

6. *Multiple choice.* An incubator was programmed so that its temperature inside starts to rise at 84°F and then rise for 4 hours at a constant rate of 2°F per hour until reaching a maximum temperature of 92°F. The temperature then falls at the same rate. Which equation gives the temperature $f(t)$ in terms of time t? **c**

(a) $f(t) = |t|$ (b) $f(t) = |92 - t|$ (c) $f(t) = -2|t - 4| + 92$

Representations Objective I

In 7 and 8, graph the function with the given equation.

7. $f(x) = |2x|$

8. $y = -|x - 2| + 2$

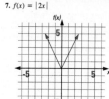

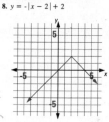

134

LESSON MASTER **13-4 A** **Questions on SPUR Objectives**
See pages 821-823 for objectives.

Properties Objective D

1. a. Give the domain of f when $f(x) = \frac{4}{x + 6}$. **all reals except -6**

b. Give the domain of g when $g(x) = \frac{x + 9}{x - 5}$. **all reals except 5**

c. Give an example of a function whose domain is the set of all real numbers except 8. **$k(x) = \frac{1}{x - 8}$**

In 2–6, a function is described. Give its domain and its range.

2. $\{(-6, 5), (-3, 1), (0, 2), (2, 10)\}$
$d = \{-6, -3, 0, 2\}$ $r = \{1, 2, 5, 10\}$

3.

$d = \{x: -1 \le x \le 3\}$
$r = \{y: 1 \le y \le 4\}$

4.

d = all reals
$r = \{y: y \ge -1\}$

5. $g(x) = \sqrt{x + 8}$
$d = \{x: x \ge 0\}$ $r = \{y: y \ge 8\}$

6. $s(x) = \frac{|x|}{x}$
$d = \{x: x \ne 0\}$ $r = \{-1, 1\}$

Uses Objective E

7. The table at the right shows a system used to describe the intensity of a hurricane.

Category	Wind Speed
1 (weak)	74–95 mph
2 (moderate)	96–110 mph
3 (strong)	111–130 mph
4 (very strong)	131–155 mph
5 (devastating)	156+ mph

a. Give three possible (category, wind speed) ordered pairs.
Sample: (1, 80), (1, 85), (4, 140)

b. Give three possible (wind speed, category) ordered pairs.
Sample: (80, 1), (85, 1), (140, 4)

c. Is either set of all ordered pairs in Parts **a** and **b** a function? Explain why or why not. **Sample is given.**
Part b; for each *x*, there is exactly one *y*.

135

LESSON MASTER **13-5 A** **Questions on SPUR Objectives**
See pages 821-823 for objectives.

Uses Objective F

1. Gregor Mendel was the first scientist to connect probability to genetics. He crossed snapdragons that have red flowers with snapdragons that have white flowers. He obtained three kinds of offspring: snapdragons with red flowers, snapdragons with white flowers, and snapdragons with pink flowers. He found $P(\text{red}) = \frac{1}{4}$ and $P(\text{white}) = \frac{1}{4}$ where $P(\text{color})$ means the probability that the offspring of snapdragons will have flowers of color x.

a. What is $P(\text{pink})$? **$\frac{1}{2}$**

b. What is the range of this function? **$\{\frac{1}{4}, \frac{1}{2}\}$**

2. Two dice are tossed. Find $P(\text{sum is even})$ and $P(\text{sum is odd})$. Explain your method.

$P(\text{sum is even}) = \frac{1}{2}$; $P(\text{sum is odd}) = \frac{1}{2}$; sample explanation: There are 36 outcomes, with 18 even sums and 18 odd sums; $\frac{18}{36} = \frac{1}{2}$.

3. Suppose for families with 2 children, if $P(n)$ = the probability that n children in the family can roll their tongue, then $P(1) = \frac{1}{8}$ and $P(2) = \frac{1}{64}$.

a. What does $P(0)$ represent?
Sample: the probability that neither child can roll his or her tongue

b. Find $P(0)$. **$\frac{55}{64}$**

136

▶

▶ **LESSON MASTER 13-5 A** *page 2*

Representations Objective I

4. The fair spinner at the right is divided into six congruent parts. The point value of each region is labeled. Let $P(n)$ = probability of getting n points on a spin.

   a. Find $P(0)$, $P(5)$, and $P(10)$.

   $P(0) = \frac{1}{6}$, $P(5) = \frac{1}{3}$,

   $P(10) = \frac{1}{2}$

   b. Graph $P(n)$.

5. A cookie jar contains 15 oatmeal cookies, 6 chocolate-chip cookies, and 9 peanut-butter cookies. You reach in and choose a cookie at random.

   a. Find P(choosing an oatmeal cookie).

   $\frac{1}{2}$

   b. Graph the probability it will be oatmeal (OM), chocolate chip (CC), or peanut butter (PB).

6. There are three stoplights on Meg's way to work. Let $P(n)$ = the probability that Meg will have to stop at exactly n red lights.

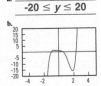

   a. What is the probability that Meg will not have to stop at all three lights?

   0.8

   b. What is $P(0) + P(1) + P(2) + P(3)$?

   1

137

LESSON MASTER **13-6 A**

Questions on SPUR Objectives
See pages 821-823 for objectives.

Representations Objective J

In 1 and 2, an equation is given. a. Complete the table of x- and y-values. b. Plot the ordered pairs and connect them with a smooth curve. c. Describe the graph. **Sample graphs and descriptions are given.**

1. $y = x^4 - x^3 + 2x^2 - 2x + 4$

   a.
x	y
-3	136
-2	40
-1	10
0	4
1	4
2	16
3	70

   b.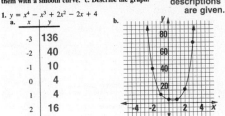

   c. Graph has at least one curve. It has no x-intercepts; y-intercept is 4.

2. $y = x^3 + 2x^2 - 4x - 5$

   a.
x	y
-3	-2
-2	3
-1	0
0	-5
1	-6
2	3
3	28

   b.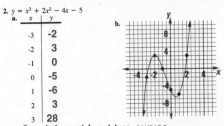

   c. Graph has at least two curves. The x-intercepts are at $\approx$ -2.8, -1, and 1.8; y-intercept is -5.

138 ▶

▶ **LESSON MASTER 13-6 A** *page 2*

In 3–6, use an automatic grapher. A function is given. a. Find a window which shows all the x- and y-intercepts of the function. b. Draw the graph of this function as it appears on your automatic grapher. **Sample windows are given.**

3. $f(x) = x^3 + 3x^2 + 3x + 2$

   a. $-5 \leq x \leq 5$

   $-10 \leq y \leq 10$

   b.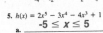

4. $g(x) = x^4 - 2x^2 + 1$

   a. $-5 \leq x \leq 5$

   $-10 \leq y \leq 10$

   b.

5. $h(x) = 2x^5 - 3x^4 - 4x^3 + 1$

   a. $-5 \leq x \leq 5$

   $-20 \leq y \leq 20$

   b.

6. $y = x^3 - 2x + 1$

   a. $-5 \leq x \leq 5$

   $-1 \leq y \leq 3$

   b.

139

LESSON MASTER **13-7 A**

Questions on SPUR Objectives
See pages 821-823 for objectives.

Skills Objective B

1. Write a calculator key sequence to find tan 48°.

   Sample: 48 [tan]

In 2 and 3, round to the nearest hundredth.

2. tan 15°   0.27

3. tan 71.5°   2.99

Uses Objective G

4.

   a. Find the length of segment RP.   12

   b. Find the tangent of angle P.

   $\frac{5}{12}$, or ≈ 0.42

In 5 and 6, find the slope of the line.

5.

   ≈ 1.60

6.

   ≈ 0.84

7. What is the tangent of the acute angle formed by the line $5x - 2y = 3$ and the positive ray of the x-axis?   2.5

8.

   When Roberto stands 30 feet away from the flagpole, he has to look up 29° to see the top. His eyes are 5 ft above the ground. How high is the flagpole?

   ≈ 21 feet

140

LESSON MASTER **13-8 A**

Skills Objective B

In 1–6, give a decimal approximation rounded to the nearest hundredth.

1. $\cos 12°$

    0.98

2. $\sin 78°$

    0.98

3. the reciprocal of 6.02

    0.17

4. $\log(0.125)$

    -0.90

5. $12!$

    479,001,600

6. $\log(1000)$

    3

In 7–10, give an example of a real number that is *not* in the domain of the function and whose values are found by pressing the indicated calculator key. If all real numbers are in the domain of the function, write "all."

Samples are given for 8-10.

7. $\boxed{x^2}$

    all

8. $\boxed{!}$

    2.7

9. $\boxed{1/x}$

    0

10. $\boxed{\sqrt{}}$

    -6

11. There is a function related to the common logarithm called the *natural logarithm*, or $y = \ln x$. The natural logarithm of a number x is the power to which the special number $e \approx 2.718$ must be raised to equal the number x. Experiment with your calculator to find the domain of this function. The key on your calculator for the natural logarithm function is labeled $\boxed{\ln}$.

    all positive real numbers

In 12 and 13, use an automatic grapher to graph the function. a. Determine the domain of the function. b. Determine the range of the function. c. Give the values of x, if any, that will produce an error message on your grapher.

12. $y = \sin x$

    a. **all real numbers**

    b. **$y: \{-1 \le y \le 1\}$**

    c. **none**

13. $y = \log x$

    a. **all positive reals**

    b. **all real numbers**

    c. **non-positive reals**

ALGEBRA © Scott, Foresman and Company

141

178